New First Certificate

Masterclass

Workbook
With Answers

Simon Haines

Barbara Stewart

OXFORD UNIVERSITY PRESS

Acknowledgements

The Publisher and authors would like to thank the following for their kind permission to reproduce articles, extracts and adaptations of copyright material:

p.4 extract from 'In the firing line' © The Observer Magazine; p.6 extract from 'Blind jumper' © The Independent; p.6 extract from 'Taking the leap' © The Guardian; p.9 from John Lancaster: 'Eating out' © The Observer; p.10 from Gay Search: 'July 2026' © Living Magazine; p.12 extract from 'Why you could get sick of immortality' © The Guardian; p.14 from Robert Matthew: 'The wind' © Focus Magazine; p.16 from Lesley Gillilan: 'Neighbours from hell' in The Guardian Weekend © The Guardian; p.19 adapted from James Davies: 'Hollywood cashes in on tragic Willy' © The Daily Express; p.22 adapted from 'Couple abandoned children' © The Guardian; p.24 adapted from Clare Campbell: 'A daughter's story', Marie Claire/Robert Harding Syndication; p.30 from Alison Turnball: 'Record-breakers' © Focus Magazine; p.32 extract from 'The mysterious hitchhiker' © The Guardian; p.33 adapted from article by David Harrison: 'It's Alderknitti by a shorthead' © The Observer; p.36 extract from: 'Somebody's stolen my daughter' and p.39 extract from: 'Zoo's TV starlet Belinda' both courtesy of The Guardian; p.42 adapted from Louise Clarke: 'How to get the job of your dreams' from National Student Extra June 1994, with permission; p.46 adaptation of 'Me and my job' reproduced from Woman © Woman/Solo Syndication, by permission; p.47 extract from 'Opportunity for adventure with Oxventure' with kind permission of author, John Havens, in World Magazine (BBC); p.48 extract from 'Goods worth £60,000' and extract from '80 year old tramp', both courtesy of The Guardian; p.49 extract from 'Los Angeles pizza-filcher' by Phil Reeves © The Independent; p.49 extract from 'Pistol-packing eight year old' and extract from 'Village vigilantes' both © The Guardian, with permission; p.51 adapted from 'Prepare to stop' © Health Education Authority; p.52 extract from 'Cloth doll rides shotgun' by Phil Reeves © The Independent; p.56 adapted from 'Attractions in the Cotswolds' reproduced with permission from Art Works; p.60 adapted from 'Finland is for you' reproduced with permission from the Finnish Tourist Board, 30-35 Pall Mall, London SW1Y 5LT; p.62 from Ian Ridpath:'UFO sightings' © Focus Magazine; p.66 adapted from 'The story of your Dr Martens' courtesy of R. Griggs Group Ltd; p.68 extract from 'The Biosphere experiment' by Phil Reeves © The Independent; p.71 adapted from 'Eight things you might regret saying' in The Mail on Sunday You Magazine © Mail on Sunday/Solo Syndication; p.71 adapted from John Kercher: 'Missionaries of vision' © Hello! Magazine; p.72 adapted from 'Bath-time TV', by kind permission of Which? Magazine; p.74 adapted from Mike Thomson: 'Walk on the dark side' © The Observer; p.76 adapted from 'Spring festivals' in Education Guardian © The Guardian; p.84 extract from Barry Hugill: 'The four-year-old undergraduate' © The Observer; p.88 adapted from '10 Hot tips for staying cool at exam time' reproduced with acknowledgement to Essex Careers and Business Partnership Limited 16+ Magazine, issue 95-96; p.91 extract from 'Music drives men round the bend too fast' © The Guardian; p.91 adapted from Julian Coleman: 'This tale is not to be sniffed at' © The Early Times.

Although every effort has been made to trace and contact copyright holders before publication, this has not been possible in the following cases. We apologize for any apparent infringement of copyright and if notified, the publisher will be pleased to rectify any errors or omissions at the earliest opportunity.

p.40 adapted from article 'It can't be true', source unknown; p.59 adapted article 'Need to conform' in The Indy; p.70 adapted from Gareth Herincx: 'Kanga Killers' in Scoop; p.82 extract from Louise Hidalgo: 'The mysterious power of the brain', in The Indy.

Illustrations by:
Sophie Grillet
Andy Hammond
Stephen Player

Location photography by:
Emily Andersen

The Publisher and authors would like to thank the following for their permission to reproduce photographs: Allsport UK Ltd/Mike Hewitt, Mike Powell, Associated Press, Cotswold Countryside Collection, Mary Evans Picture Library, The Ronald Grant Archive, Robert Harding Picture Library, The Hutchison Library/Noman Lomax, Orbis International, Oxventure, Rex Features Ltd/Tony Larkin, Nils Jorgensen, Frank Spooner Pictures Ltd/Gavin Smith, Sygma, Alison Williams.

The Publisher and authors would like to thank the following for their valuable advice and detailed comments on the manuscript: Mark Harrison; Sarah Keith; Nina Rosa da Silva; Clare West.

Contents

1 Description

Reading

1 Before you read

The photographs show a *human cannonball* flying through the air. Do you think this circus act is as dangerous as it looks?

2 Reading

Read the text quickly to find out if it answers this question.
As you read, make a note of five difficult words you would like to check in your dictionary later.

3 Comprehension

Read questions 1–6 below to make sure you understand what kind of information each question is asking for. Then read the text again and find the parts containing the information you need. For each question, choose the best answer, A, B, C or D.

1 Why is Osci Tabak a very special circus performer?
   A He does not follow safety regulations.
   B He makes almost no mistakes in his work.
   C He may be the only remaining human cannonball in Europe.
   D He works in an exceptionally small room.

2 Council officers are worried about Osci Tabak, because they think
   A he may hurt himself.
   B he may hurt other people.
   C he may damage public property.
   D he may land in a public place.

3 How did Osci Tabak become a cannonball?
   A He learnt the techniques from someone in his family.
   B He took part in an act with a Polish cannonball.
   C He took the place of a performer who had been injured.
   D He joined a group of Hungarian cannonballs.

In the *firing line.*

Human cannonballs have always had hard lives. Fitted tight into the barrel of a gun, then shot 30 metres through the air towards a net, night after night, with almost no room for error.

   For Osci Tabak, who is pictured above as Cannonball Captain Apollo in Gerry Cottle's Circus, and is said to be Europe's last human cannonball, life is even harder than usual.

4 What must be done before Osci is fired from the gun?
   A The target must be carefully positioned.
   B The gun must be nowhere near the tent poles.
   C The circus tent must be supported by special poles.
   D The gun must be pointed accurately.

5 What definite changes to Osci's act are planned for the future?
   A He is going to train his son to take over from him as a cannonball.
   B He is going to do his act without being able to see where he is going.
   C He is going to retire before he has an accident and let his son take over.
   D He is going to be fired with his son from a double gun.

6 Which is the best summary of Osci's view of what he does?
   A He is proud of his unusual act.
   B He is fully aware of the risks he takes.
   C His act is just a job to him.
   D He doesn't care whether he has an accident or not.

EXAM TIP

When you have made your choice of answer, try to work out why the other three answers are wrong.

Bureaucrats are particularly keen to make sure that his unusual act follows strict safety regulations.

"We are most concerned," says a spokesman for Brent Council's Health and Safety Department, "about the possibility of injury to the public, for instance if the cannonball lands among them. However, the cannonball has been appearing in Potters Bar for two weeks, and we have had no reports of low-flying circus performers."

Osci, who is 42 years old, has been firing himself out of gun barrels for years. Brought up in a Hungarian circus family, he became a cannonball at the age of 12 when his acrobatics teacher, a Polish cannonball, was badly wounded after being misfired. "The gun was only powered by a strong piece of elastic – like an enormous catapult," Osci relates sadly. "He missed the net at the other end and was thrown into the ring, losing an eye. So he had to teach me how to take over his act."

According to Osci, the essential first step is to line up the gun correctly. If the aim is accurate, Osci does not have to worry about hitting the poles holding up the circus tent or, what would be worse, flying off-target and into other performers or the audience.

Zooming out of the cannon at 90 kph, Osci has to focus on the net and fall into it at precisely the right moment, or he will fly past and miss it entirely. According to the circus manager, this is not easy, even for an expert like Osci. "He's like a bullet," Martin says, "and if he goes the wrong way, he could write off members of the public."

But Captain Apollo has yet to have an in-flight accident; clearly the greatest danger in his act is the danger to himself. This century, cannonballing has claimed at least 26 lives. "I'm lucky to have survived so long," says Osci, who flies without a helmet. "But once I am in the barrel I forget everything. The presenter shouts 'Five, four, three, two, one, fire!' And that's it. I go with a bang."

For his next stunt, the Captain will be fired out of a cannon wearing a blindfold and with a bag over his head. "My son will shout out when I must fall into the net. Otherwise I will break my neck," he says cheerily.

The Tabak family does not get off that lightly: Osci is thinking of ordering a double-barrelled cannon so that his son, Osci Junior, an up-and-coming cannonball, can be fired out at the same time as his father.

4 Vocabulary

A Fill the gaps in these sentences with appropriate prepositions.
There are similar phrases in the text.

1 People who are accident-prone are a danger _____ themselves and others.

2 No one's perfect. There's always room _____ improvements.

3 Mozart started composing music _____ the age of seven.

4 There's a public telephone box _____ the end of our road.

5 Without my glasses I just can't focus properly _____ anything.

6 Though the train crashed at high speed, there were no injuries _____ any of the passengers.

B Work out the meaning of these compound adjectives from the text and write a phrase with approximately the same meaning. An example is given. Then use your dictionary to check your ideas.

1 low-flying
which flies low or close to the ground

2 off-target
_____

3 in-flight
_____

4 double-barrelled
_____

5 up-and-coming
_____

Grammar

1 Missing prepositions

Fill the gaps in this newspaper report with suitable prepositions.

Blind jumper

Betty Wilson, a 70-year-old blind great-grandmother (1)_____ Edinburgh, became the oldest person (2)_____ Britain to do a bungee jump. She jumped (3)_____ a 165 foot crane (4)_____ Washington (5)_____ the North-East (6)_____ England.
Straight (7)_____ her jump, she said: "It helps being blind – you can't see how far you might fall."

2 Use of English

A Read the text below quickly.
• Who is John West?

_____

• What does he do when people jump?

_____

B Read the text again and fill each gap with one word only. An example is given.

After bungee-jumping:
bridge-swinging

Bored with caving or mountaineering? Why (0) _*not*_ try bridge-swinging? It is quite unlike bungee-jumping, where you go up and (1)_____ like a yo-yo. It is a (2)_____ like parachuting without a parachute. Here's (3)_____ a member of one group describes it:
"Wrap a climber's harness around your hips, attach a 50-metre rope, then balance (4)_____ on the top rail of a disused railway bridge, trying (5)_____ to look at the river more than 30 metres below. And (6)_____ John West shouts 'Dive!', fling yourself out and away and down and under and up the other side."

John West is the man at the other end of the rope (7)_____ controls your descent, letting out just (8)_____ rope as you swing, then dropping

you neatly on to the river bank. It is over in a (9)_____ seconds.

Beginners tend (10)_____ jump backwards so they can't see the drop. More experienced swingers go head-first, with their arms and legs spread out.

Most meetings attract new members, like Ian Edmunds, aged 28, who decided to jump (11)_____ it sounded like fun. He remembers it well: "(12)_____ was terrifying. I almost fell off the rail before I was properly attached to the rope."

Ian Green recalls his first jump just (13)_____ clearly: "I flung myself into space and felt an incredible jerk as the rope took my weight. Before I realised what (14)_____ happening, I landed on my back – I wasn't hurt at all."

John West, the organizer says: "We've (15)_____ had an accident yet. And I'm prepared to bet we never will."

3 Odd one out

➤ Grammar reference, Student's Book, page 200

In each of these sets of three sentences, two sentences have a similar meaning and one has a different meaning. Put a cross (X) next to the sentences with different meanings.

1 a He's always telling other people what to do. ___
  b He's telling other people what to do. ___
  c He keeps telling other people what to do. ___
2 a I used to walk to school every day. ___
  b I would walk to school every day. ___
  c I've walked to school every day. ___
3 a We're going to the beach in the summer. ___
  b We tend to go to the beach in the summer. ___
  c We usually go to the beach in the summer. ___
4 a I used to get up early. ___
  b I am used to getting up early. ___
  c I am accustomed to getting up early. ___
5 a I know children spend all their money on sweets and chocolate. ___
  b I know children are going to spend all their money on sweets and chocolate. ___
  c I know children will spend all their money on sweets and chocolate. ___

4 Habitual actions

These sentences all describe past or present habitual actions. Fill each gap with one of the words below. You may have to change the form of these words.

keep   tend   used   will   would

1 When I was a child I _____ to enjoy going to the cinema.
2 Even nowadays trains _____ to be late when the weather is bad.
3 The dog next door _____ barking. It's really annoying.
4 If she has nothing special to do, my mother _____ spend all day cooking.
5 Ten years ago I _____ frequently work right through the night, but I can't do it now.
6 People with fair skin _____ to burn easily if they sunbathe for too long.
7 I don't know why, but I _____ thinking it's Friday today.
8 In the past, people rarely _____ to wash their hair.

Vocabulary

➤ Vocabulary reference, Student's Book, page 215

1 Wordsearch

Find the ten 'place' words in this wordsearch. Words can run forwards or backwards, up or down, or diagonally. Here are the definitions.

1 adjective used to describe a built-up area like a town
2 a town on the coast with a harbour
3 an area of land between two hills or mountains, often with a river running along it
4 a single-storey house
5 a very tall, modern city building
6 a room used for sleeping and living in; a very small apartment
7 an area of land belonging to a house, often used for growing flowers or vegetables
8 a residential area outside the centre of a town or city
9 a high area of land, but not as high as a mountain
10 adjective used to describe a country area away from towns

P	S	U	B	U	R	B	A	L	T
O	H	O	A	U	R	B	A	N	O
R	Y	E	L	L	A	V	N	I	S
T	I	B	U	N	G	A	L	O	W
O	S	S	B	J	P	F	E	L	I
H	B	E	D	S	I	T	C	A	E
P	I	N	E	D	R	A	G	R	T
E	S	L	A	R	W	E	D	U	P
E	T	B	L	D	R	P	L	R	M
R	E	P	A	R	C	S	Y	K	S

2 Overheard remarks

In which places might you hear these?
1 . . . and about a kilo of grapes, please.
2 When did you say the flight landed in Washington?
3 Can you recommend something for a sore throat, please?
4 A day return to Oxford, please.
5 . . . two packets of white envelopes and a box of paper clips.
6 I'll have two lamb chops and some sausages.
7 Two first class stamps. And could you weigh this parcel for me, please?
8 I'd like a large piece of cod.

3 Jumbled words

Read the definitions and sort the letters to make some more words for places.
1 a large building where there are council offices
WONT ALHL

_____

2 adjective used to describe a house that is not joined to other houses
EACHTEDD

_____

3 some high car parks have ten or more of these
RESSTOY

_____

4 a large, important church
THECRADAL

_____

5 where to go to catch a train
WALIRAY NATTIOS

_____

6 a large shop selling many different kinds of goods
PRAMTENTED RESTO

_____

7 a geographical area or a part of a country
NIGERO

_____

8 a small, narrow river
MASTER

_____

9 a high, often steep area of rock next to the sea
FLICF

_____

10 land along the edge of the sea
HORSE

_____

4 Phrasal verbs

A Match the phrasal verbs 1–6 with meanings a–f.
1 get through ____
2 settle down ____
3 grow up ____
4 turn into ____
5 go on ____
6 pick up ____

a change from a child into an adult
b become
c catch, become infected
d consume
e start living a quiet, stable life
f happen

B Now complete the following sentences with the correct form of one of the phrasal verbs in A above.
1 You've got a terrible cough. Where did you

_____ it _____?

2 Some people say that children these days

_____ much more quickly than they used to.

3 There's a dreadful noise coming from our

neighbours' flat. I've no idea what _____.

4 Famous people often find it difficult to _____

and live a normal life.

5 My dream was quite pleasant to start with, but it

quickly _____ a nightmare.

6 I don't know why you've bought so much food for

the party. We'll never _____ it all.

Writing

Paragraphing and punctuation

➤ Student's Book, page 20

A Read this description of a London restaurant and add the necessary punctuation. The missing punctuation marks are capital letters, full stops, commas, apostrophes and quotation marks.

Madhu's Brilliant is an indian restaurant in southall an area of london which someone once called britains best-known asian suburb it is run by the younger members of the anand family whose father madhu started the original restaurant it is a glass-fronted building on southalls lively south road downstairs is brownish and darker upstairs is blue and white with a bar and a set of tables we started our meal with alu gobi which is potatoes and cauliflower in a sauce of tomato and yoghurt and then for our main course we had chicken and prawn curry we finished off with kulfi which is a pistachio-flavoured indian ice-cream everything was expertly prepared and tasted delicious the cooking at the brilliant as is often the case in above average indian restaurants comes from one region in this case the punjab i would strongly recommend going to the brilliant with a few friends to get the benefit of ordering a wider range of dishes from the menu

B Read the text again and divide it into four paragraphs.

C Write a description of a restaurant, café or bar you know well. Follow the paragraph plan below and use the questions to help you. Write 120–180 words in all.

Paragraph 1   A brief description of the place

What is its name?
Who is the owner?
Who else works there?
What is the atmosphere like?
When did you first go there?

_____

_____

_____

_____

Paragraph 2   The location

Where is it? Which part of town is it in?
How near is it to where you live?

_____

_____

_____

Paragraph 3   The food and drink

What can you get to eat and drink there?
Are there any specialities?
Is it good value for money?

_____

_____

_____

_____

Paragraph 4   Advice about going there

Where is the best place to sit?
When is it very busy?

_____

_____

_____

_____

EXAM TIP

When you have finished a piece of writing, check grammar, spelling and punctuation.

Future

Reading

1 Before you read

You are going to read an article about life in the future. Make a list of some words you think it might include. Two examples are given.

computers _____ _____
travel _____ _____
_____ _____
_____ _____
_____ _____
_____

2 Reading

Read the article and tick all the words you predicted correctly.

3 Comprehension

Choose from sentences A–H the one which fits each gap in the article. There is one sentence that does not fit anywhere.

A *You* may be married with 2.2 children, but this won't be the norm any more.

B This would make it possible to go from London to New York for the evening.

C What he didn't know was that the invention of the motor car was just round the corner.

D Eventually you might be able to watch holograms which actually move.

E They'll be fitted with computers to tell us how efficiently we're driving, and if there's anything wrong with the engine.

F Offices, too, will go electronic with the result that paper will almost completely disappear.

G This is an attractive idea for a parent with young children who wants to go on working.

H But two major themes seem to emerge from almost every prediction made.

2026

We may not be driving around in hover-cars or eating tablets instead of tasty food, but in 30 years' time some things will be very different.

The four-day working week will certainly be a reality, so we'll have a lot more time for leisure activities. But what else will be different?

When you think about the future, remember that progress has never moved in straight lines, and that history is full of unexpected developments. Take the early American futurologist who predicted that if the horse traffic went on increasing at the same rate, by 1950 the streets of New York would be two metres deep in manure! ⬚ **1**

If you ask a hundred people to look into the future, you will probably get a hundred different answers. ⬚ **2**

The first is variety in every aspect of our lives. We'll probably be living in what futurologists have called a 'multi-option society'. ⬚ **3** It will simply be one of a number of choices, along with living in groups and living alone.

The other huge influence on our lives will be micro technology – computers and telecommunications. Take work, for instance. Factories will be run largely by

2026

EXAM TIP

To match missing sentences to the correct gaps, look first for strong topic connections and then for grammatical links.

robots, so they'll be cleaner places for the few people who work in them. [4] More people will work from home at computers linked to a head office. Their homes may even be turned into 'electronic cottages', with Mum, Dad and even the children all sharing one or maybe two jobs.

As for travel, it's likely that space-shuttle technology will be used in normal air travel, with rocket motors being used to get an aircraft through the earth's atmosphere to an height of 300 kilometres. Here the plane could accelerate up to 15,000 kph before re-entering the atmosphere and landing normally. [5]

Cars will still be with us, although their body panels will probably be plastic so that we can fit on new ones when they're damaged, or when we get bored with the colour or style. [6] And, instead of petrol, they could run on anything from electricity to methane gas.

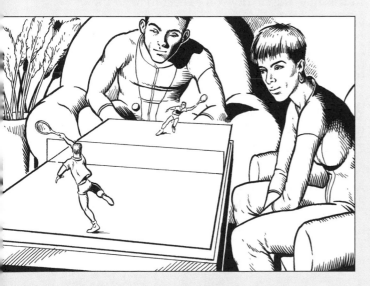

One of the most exciting ideas of all is the hologram – a three-dimensional image created by lasers. [7] Can you imagine watching miniature tennis players playing the Australian Open finals in your own living-room?

4 Vocabulary

A Find two- or three-word phrases in the article which have the following meanings. An example is given.

1 road vehicles which move along on a cushion of air
   hover-cars

2 things that people enjoy doing in their free time
   _____

3 a social community in which there are many choices _____

4 the main or central building of an organization
   _____

5 the outside parts of a car _____

6 a picture which has length, width and depth
   _____

B Fill the gaps in these sentences with appropriate prepositions. Similar phrases are used in the article.

1 I enjoy reading anything _____ children's comics to serious poems.

2 The teacher I had in my first year at school had an enormous influence _____ me.

3 _____ 20 years' time I hope I'll be running my own business.

4 My sister has only been learning Spanish for three weeks, but she's improving _____ an incredible rate.

5 I'm really bored _____ my hairstyle, so I'm going to the hairdresser's on Saturday.

6 Our school is linked _____ a similar school in Australia.

7 I'm so busy at work these days that I never seem to have any time _____ relaxation.

Grammar

1 Use of English

A Read the text quickly and decide which of these statements best summarizes Professor Evans' ideas about long life.

1 It will be possible and desirable for people to live beyond the age of 115.
2 It will not be possible for people to live beyond the age of 115.
3 It will be possible but not necessarily good for people to live to beyond the age of 115.

B Now read the text again more carefully and fill each gap with one suitable word. An example is given.

Who wants to live forever ?

A leading researcher into old age has warned that the dream of living forever, or at least much longer than at present, could turn into a curse rather than a blessing. It may become possible (0)___*to*___ lengthen the average human life by manipulating genes – but (1)_____ we gain may not be worth (2)_____ price we would have to pay.

Professor John Grimley Evans believes that currently, maximum life expectation is 115, but that with gene therapy (3)_____ might be possible to extend this. (4)_____ professor says, however, that a sensible lifestyle can extend the average lifespan of everyone at (5)_____ moment.

'We know a lot already (6)_____ how people's lifestyles affect their lifespan. There is increasing evidence to suggest that sensible lifestyles are effective in later life as well (7)_____ in early and middle life.'

'It is never (8)_____ late to gain some benefit from giving up smoking, from drinking less alcohol, from taking up sensible patterns of diet and exercise and from controlling body weight. We already know (9)_____ to lengthen human life.'

The professor believes that the process of lengthening life (10)_____ means of gene therapy might bring dangers with it. If gene therapy affected only one part of (11)_____ human body but not all of it, people might be physically capable of living longer, but would start to deteriorate mentally (12)_____ a much earlier age.

EXAM TIP

On the second reading, read the text slowly. Fill the gaps you are confident about first.

2 Future

➤ Grammar reference, Student's Book, pages 200–201

A What would you say in these situations?

1 You intend to go to Australia for your holiday next year.
_____

2 You have already arranged to meet your sister this evening.
_____

3 At this time tomorrow you expect to be in the process of walking to school.
_____

4 The weather has become very cold and the sky has turned black. This means snow very soon.
_____

5 You've looked at the train timetable for the weekend. It says the departure time of your train is 7.15 in the morning.
_____

6 After your exams have finished your plan is to travel round the world on a motorbike.
_____

7 There is a strong possibility of a rise in the price of food next year. This is your prediction.
_____

8 Your plane is scheduled to land at 11.15 at night.
_____

B Some of these sentences use the correct form of the future but most of them need improvement. Rewrite where necessary. An example is given.

1 We'll have a party on June 16th. It's all arranged.
We're having a party . . .

2 I'm passing my driving test if it's the last thing I do!
_____

3 The phone's ringing. I'm answering it.

4 It's a brilliant film. I'm sure you'll enjoy it.

_____

5 If they don't arrive in about ten minutes, we finish all the food.

_____

6 Hurry up – your favourite programme starts in five minutes.

_____

7 I'm sure someone's going to object if you wear jeans to work.

_____

8 What do you do when you leave school? Have you got any plans?

_____

3 Articles

Read this text and decide which gaps need an article. Fill them with *a*, *an* or *the*. Where no article is needed, write Ø.

Derek Wadlow's company does (1)_____ kind of (2)_____ jobs other people find boring. They may be boring, but they are not ordinary, that's for sure. Here are (3)_____ few of (4)_____ company's more recent jobs. They have provided (5)_____ 500 artificial but realistic corpses at (6)_____ short notice for (7)_____ horror film; they have rubbed (8)_____ small printing error off 10,000 Arabic banknotes; they've made (9)_____ holes in several hundred eggs, blown out (10)_____ inside and stuffed (11)_____ shells with (12)_____ rolled-up advertising leaflet. Derek Wadlow's next project could be (13)_____ equally challenging one. "We've got to set up quarter of (14)_____ million dominoes in (15)_____ shape of (16)_____ company name, then our client will film them falling down," explains Derek Wadlow. "I am worried about not being able to find (17)_____ area large enough to accommodate all (18)_____ dominoes."

Vocabulary

1 Puzzle

➤ Vocabulary reference, Student's Book, page 215

All the answers to this puzzle are connected with the weather. Read the clues and write the missing words. Some letters are given to help you.

Across
1 a short fall of rain
2 amount of rain in one place over a period of time
3 often accompanies thunder during a storm
4 one bit of snow
5 a harmful effect of staying out in the sun for too long
6 a light type of fog
7 a prediction about the weather
8 bright light from the sun
9 the opposite of rainy

Down
10 a small ball of hard ice which falls like rain or snow

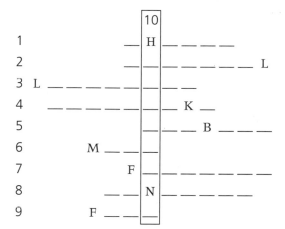

2 Use of English

A Read this text about the wind. Don't try to fill the gaps until you have answered these questions.

1 Which two dates are mentioned in the text?

_____

_____

2 How many deaths were there in the most recent storm? _____

The power of
nature

The wind controls our planet's weather and climate, but how much do we understand about this complex force, which can kill and spread fear?

On the night of 15 October 1987, the south of England was struck by the (1)_____ winds it had known for over two hundred years. (2)_____ of over 130 km/h blew through the region. Nineteen people were killed, £1.5 billion-worth of (3)_____ was caused and 19 million trees were (4)_____ in just a few hours.

Although people thought of this as a hurricane, the winds of 1987 were only (5)_____ storm force. They are far better known than the much more serious storms of 25 January 1990, when most of Britain was hit by daytime winds of up to 173 km/h. On this (6)_____, 47 people were killed, even though, unlike in 1987, the weather forecasters issued accurate (7)_____.

(8)_____ weather events such as these are dramatic reminders of the power of the wind. It is one part of the weather that people generally do not (9)_____ a second thought to, but across the world the wind (10)_____ a crucial role in people's lives.

B Now read the text again and fill the gaps with the most suitable word or phrase, A,B,C or D.

1 A heaviest
   B fastest
   C strongest
   D quickest

2 A Blows
   B Hits
   C Clouds
   D Gusts

3 A hurt
   B injury
   C destruction
   D damage

4 A blown down
   B cut down
   C knocked down
   D blown up

5 A powerful
   B severe
   C serious
   D dangerous

6 A occasion
   B event
   C accident
   D incident

7 A threats
   B warnings
   C news
   D signs

8 A Extreme
   B Excessive
   C Extravagant
   D Exaggerated

9 A have
   B make
   C put
   D give

10 A has
   B makes
   C plays
   D does

3 Phrasal verbs

Replace the words in italics in these sentences with one of the phrasal verbs from the list. There is an extra verb that you do not need and you must use two of the verbs twice.

break up	get through	go on
put up	settle down	turn into

1 It's certain that the government will *raise* taxes next year. _____

2 Somehow we managed to *spend* all our money on the first day of our holiday. _____

3 I know it's cold and rainy now but I'm sure it's going to *become* a really nice day. _____

4 If you come to London, I'll be happy to *accommodate* you for the night. _____

5 After we *finish school* at the end of next week, I'm going to get a part-time job in a supermarket. _____

6 After the third goal, the crowd stood up and cheered before they *became still* again. _____

7 I'm sorry to *bring* the meeting *to an end*, but I've got to leave in five minutes. _____

Writing

Formal and informal styles

➤ Student's Book, page 32

A Read the five extracts and decide where each might be from. Choose from this list.

1 reminder card sent by a dentist _____
2 passport application form _____
3 holiday brochure _____
4 formal letter _____
5 mail-order catalogue _____
6 invitation to a reception _____
7 memo about hotel arrangements _____

---

a It gives me great pleasure to inform you that you have been chosen to receive a special award, and a cheque in your name is waiting to be claimed now.

---

b All items can be ordered on your regular order form. Simply write the code number(s) of your chosen item(s) in the appropriate boxes.

---

c We would be most grateful if you could call or telephone at your earliest convenience to make an appointment.

---

d Your accommodation has been guaranteed and will be held for late arrival. Any changes should be notified in advance to avoid additional charges.

---

e Take your completed form, photographs, required documents and fee in person to one of the following offices.

B Read the extracts again and underline the formal equivalents of these words and phrases. The number of the extract is in brackets and an underlined example has been done for you.

1 I'm very pleased (a)
2 tell (a)
3 get (a)
4 everything (b)
5 the things you want (b)
6 as soon as you can (c)
7 extra cost (d)
8 official papers needed (e)

C Write an informal letter to your British or American pen friend, inviting him or her to stay with you and your family. Write 120–180 words in all.

1 Decide what you are going to write and make notes.
2 Make a list of some of the informal words and phrases you could use.
3 Write your letter, following this paragraph plan.

Paragraph 1   Thank your pen friend for their last letter.
         Ask about health and recent news.

_____
_____
_____
_____

Paragraph 2   Make the invitation, describing one or two things you might do together.

_____
_____
_____

Paragraph 3   Conclude. Say you hope to see your pen friend later in the year.

_____
_____
_____
_____

4 Finally, check what you have written. Think about grammar, spelling and punctuation.

EXAM TIP

If you do not have time in the exam to do a complete plan for your writing, plan in your head what you are going to write and jot down a few useful words and phrases.

3 opinion

Reading

1 Before you read

Decide what would make someone a bad neighbour. Make a list, following the example given.

Someone who plays loud music day and night.

_____

_____

_____

_____

2 Reading

As you read this article for the first time, tick any of your ideas which are mentioned.

3 Comprehension

Read the article again carefully and choose the best answer for each question, A, B, C or D.

1 Why doesn't the writer like her next-door neighbours' dogs?
A They wake her up.
B They sometimes bark.
C They are aggressive.
D They remind her of sheep.

2 According to the report most people argue with their neighbours about
A dogs.   B noise.   C parking.   D DIY.

3 What does the article say about Mediation UK?
A It gives a lot of money to charity.
B It has over 50 groups around the world.
C It was established by the United Nations.
D It has its head office in Bristol.

4 According to the article, some people decide not to buy a house because they don't like
A the house which is next door.
B the other houses in the street.
C the appearance of the garden.
D the colour of the paint work.

Neighbours from **hell**

I used to think my little corner of urban England was somewhere I could get away from the stress and strain of modern-day life – until *they* moved in next door. There are two of them. They are white, woolly and probably have
5 sharp teeth as well as a loud bark. But every time their constant barking interrupts my sleep, I remind myself that, in many respects, I am lucky. The neighbours don't hold all-night parties, nor do they shout or throw crockery at each other, and though their dogs may bark, they don't bite.

10 According to a recent consumer magazine report on 'nightmare neighbours', dogs are the fifth most common source of bad relations between neighbours. Noise of any description heads the list of complaints, followed by DIY* enthusiasts, parking disputes, and arguments over house extensions.

15 So what alternatives are there? One is to take legal action. But this can be time-consuming and expensive and does nothing to improve already difficult relationships. The other alternatives are to sell up and go, or to try to reach a solution with the help of someone neutral. Mediation UK –
20 the United Nations equivalent of garden fence conflicts – was set up in 1984 to help resolve community disagreements. The Bristol-based charity acts as an umbrella organisation for 60 regional groups, which are

5 What does 'it' in line 39 refer to?
A the colour scheme.
B the garden.
C the situation.
D the house.

staffed by trained volunteers. In most cases, officers find that lack of communication is the main cause of conflict and that peace can be negotiated.

David Nation of Plymouth Mediation points to poor public housing and widespread unemployment as additional factors. He also reports more cases of complaints from people who live in flats. Large houses built in the nineteenth century and designed as single-occupation family homes have, he says, been converted into flats with little or no attention to sound insulation. Dividing walls are paper thin and hardly block out sound at all.

Buyers can also be put off by the external appearance of neighbouring houses. Anything from wild, uncared for gardens to unusual external colour schemes can put off buyers – even though the offending property is next door. But it could be worse. John Gladden, of Norbury in Surrey upset his neighbours in St Oswald's Road by mounting a huge fish in fibreglass and putting it on the roof of his house. The local council argued that he should have got planning permission; residents thought the fish did nothing to improve the appearance of the neighbourhood, and war broke out. Gladden defended his right of self-expression and proceeded to install an inflatable Santa Claus and a replica tank. Sightseers poured in and homes near the suburban property can now be hard to sell.

As most problems offend the ears rather than the eyes it's surprising that so few buyers take the trouble to check out their future neighbours. Estate agents* recommend making frequent visits to the area – preferably at varying times of the day and night. It is pointless, after all, to expect people who are trying to sell their house to give an objective view of their neighbours. I recently went to view a house which looked promising – until I saw the neighbouring zoo. I decided I could live with the birds, the rabbits and the cats, but when I spotted the dogs I had my doubts. 'Do the alsatians next door bother you at all?' I asked.

'No, no,' they replied, 'not at all.'

'Oh yes they do,' insisted their six-year-old son. 'They bark all night and keep us awake.' Another lucky escape.

---

*DIY– Do it yourself; making and repairing things in your own home
*Estate agents: people who buy and sell houses for other people

6 The writer decided not to buy the house because
A it didn't have a good view.
B it was next door to a zoo.
C she didn't trust the owners.
D she disliked dogs.

7 The writer's main aim in the article is to
A inform people what to do if they have problems with their neighbours.
B describe her own problems with her neighbours.
C illustrate the types and causes of problems between neighbours.
D explain the activities of the organization Mediation UK.

EXAM TIP

Always read the text through quickly before you look at the questions and alternative answers.

4 Vocabulary

Find words or phrases in the article with these meanings. The paragraph number is given in brackets.

1 escape from something (1)_____
2 pressure and tension (1)_____
3 plates, cups, dishes, etc. (1)_____
4 arguments (2)_____
5 occurring in many different places (4)_____
6 discourage (5)_____ _____
7 disturb (6)_____

5 Text references

One of the multiple choice questions in Paper 1 Part 2 may ask you what a word in the text refers to, like question 5 in 3 opposite. What do the words in *italics* in these extracts refer to? Look back at the article to check if necessary.

1 . . . until *they* moved in next door. (line 3)
2 But *this* can be time-consuming . . . (line 16)
3 . . . *which* are staffed . . . (line 23)
4 *They* bark all night . . . (line 61)

6 Reading between the lines

Use your imagination and the information in the article to help you answer the following questions.

1 Why would it be annoying to live next-door to a DIY enthusiast?
2 Why do you think John Gladden did what he did to his house?
3 The writer says that you can't expect people who are trying to sell their house to tell you the truth about their neighbours. Why not?

Grammar

1 Gerunds and infinitives

➤ Grammar reference, Student's Book, page 201

A Put the verb in brackets in the correct form, gerund or infinitive. Remember that some verbs can take both the infinitive and the gerund but with a change of meaning.

1 Mandy isn't speaking to me because I forgot _____(get) her a birthday present. I didn't remember _____(wish) her Happy Birthday either.

2 If you don't stop _____(waste) time and at least try _____(get) the order finished today, the boss will be furious.

3 British Rail regrets _____(inform) passengers of the cancellation of the 10.06 to Glasgow Queen Street.

4 It's good _____(visit) lots of different countries because _____(travel) broadens the mind.

5 I meant _____(get up) earlier but I forgot _____(set) my alarm clock.

6 I hope Sharon won't regret _____(leave) school at 16.

7 My uncle didn't give up _____(smoke) even after the doctor told him he risked _____(have) a heart attack if he continued.

8 I can't help _____(wonder) how Andy manages _____(afford) _____(run) such an expensive car on his salary.

9 Pleased _____(meet) you. Glad _____(hear) that you're enjoying your stay.

10 Can you imagine _____(be) famous and _____(have) enough money to do whatever you like?

B In this exercise the verbs are in the correct form but the prepositions are missing. Fill each gap with an appropriate preposition from the list.

about   at   for   in   of   on   with

1 I do apologize _____ bringing Rachel but she insisted _____ coming.

2 Most politicians are extremely skilled _____ speaking in public.

3 Even though he was bored _____ doing the same thing day in day out, he was nervous _____ making a change.

4 A good salesperson is clever _____ persuading people to buy things they don't really need.

5 I'm not responsible _____ breaking the vase. It was Greg's fault.

6 Due to the increasing number of burglaries in the area, the police are warning people _____ leaving their windows open during the day.

7 Although Adrian is perfectly capable _____ getting good marks, he never does.

8 The examiner congratulated Graeme _____ passing his driving test first time.

9 Despite the strong wind, we succeeded _____ putting up our tent.

10 David is good _____ drawing but he isn't really interested _____ becoming an architect.

2 Use of English

Complete the second sentence so that it has a similar meaning to the first sentence. Use up to five words including the word you are given. Do not change this word. An example is given.

1 Jackie's heavier than she was two years ago. **put**
Jackie _____*has put on weight*_____ in the last two years.

2 Jane continued to work for the firm after the baby was born. **went**
Jane _____ for the firm after the baby was born.

3 'Are you sorry that you didn't go to university?' **regret**
'Do _____ to university?'

4 She had no intention of insulting you. **mean**
She _____ you.

5 Jason adds up figures well for a boy of his age. **good**
   Jason _____ figures for a boy of his age.
6 I have no objection to Paul coming as well. **mind**
   I do _____ as well.
7 I couldn't hear what he said because of the noise. **prevented**
   The _____ what he said.
8 Don't let Michael discourage you. **put**
   Don't _____ Michael.

3 Use of English

A Read the text through quickly and decide which heading would be more appropriate.
1 A lucky meeting
2 The day everything went wrong

B Read the text again and fill each gap with one suitable word. Remember to look for clues to the kind of word which is missing. An example is given.

Mary Evans, the Irish singer, comes from the town (0) ___*of*___ Newport. Here she remembers a special day in (1) _____ life.

'I'd been writing my own songs since (2) _____ age of 14. I am fairly ambitious and Newport (3) _____ small, so I knew I'd have to move on (4) _____ some point, but I was happy playing in local clubs.

During the autumn of 1997, when I was 18, I (5) _____ playing at a very small club called The Cat and Fiddle, (6) _____ only held about 90 people. The good thing about Newport being such (7) _____ small scene is everyone knows (8) _____ other, and through word of mouth Johnny Daly came (9) _____ see me that night. He was a very well-known producer. He spoke to (10) _____ afterwards and said (11) _____ he thought my songs sounded interesting.

Shortly afterwards, he said he wanted to make a CD. We started work in (12) _____ spare time. I didn't realize at the time (13) _____ lucky I was. I believed in (14) _____ I was doing, and now someone else believed in me, too. We had no record company and no one telling us how to make the record. Looking back, nothing (15) _____ ever been the same.'

Vocabulary

1 Use of English

Read through this text. Then use the word given in capital letters to form a word which fits in the gap. An example is given.

Priscilla Presley, (0) ___*actress*___ and widow of Elvis Presley, entered the acting profession quite (1)_____. On being asked to do a television (2)_____ for a well-known shampoo, she took what turned out to be an important (3)_____ : to take acting classes.

She did this in an attempt to overcome her acute (4)_____ at being in the public eye, but to her (5)_____ she loved every minute.

Her extreme lack of (6)_____ stemmed from the early days of her (7)_____ to Elvis, which she remembers were often spent sitting in dark, (8)_____ hotel rooms away from the glare of (9)_____, which Elvis was so anxious to avoid.

Film work, including the highly (10)_____ slapstick comedy *The Naked Gun*, quickly followed the television contract.

0 ACT	6 CONFIDENT
1 ACCIDENT	7 MARRY
2 COMMERCE	8 DEPRESS
3 DECIDE	9 PUBLIC
4 SHY	10 SUCCESS
5 AMAZE	

EXAM TIP

Think about the kind of word which is missing. If you're not sure of the answer, try out typical prefixes or endings.

2 Wordsearch

➤ Vocabulary reference, Student's Book, page 215

Find the 14 'entertainment' words in this wordsearch. Words can run forwards or backwards, up or down, or diagonally, and may overlap. Here are the definitions.

1 a film is projected onto this
2 the cheapest seats in a theatre are here
3 they play music
4 the singer in a group
5 where the orchestra plays
6 the story of a film, play or novel
7 the person who conducts the orchestra
8 a line of seats
9 an extra musical performance because of audience demand
10 a passage between seats
11 music which became popular in the Fifties
12 clap in appreciation
13 a platform actors and musicians perform on
14 make a noise of disapproval

```
M  B  O  A  I  S  L  E  P  R
V  U  S  C  R  E  E  N  A  O
O  G  S  X  O  V  U  C  R  T
C  A  L  I  W  A  B  O  O  C
A  L  R  O  C  K  T  R  L  U
L  L  A  E  T  I  P  E  L  D
I  E  A  P  P  L  A  U  D  N
S  R  N  P  L  O  T  N  L  O
T  Y  D  I  E  G  A  T  S  C
```

3 Topic vocabulary

➤ Vocabulary reference, Student's Book, page 215

Use the clues and the letters given to work out the missing words. They are all materials which are commonly used in arts and crafts.

1 You can make clothes from many different types of _ L _ _ H; for example, cotton, wool, nylon and silk.
2 Some people prefer to draw with C _ _ _ C _ _ L because it's softer than a pencil.
3 Ceramic pots are made of _ L _ _, which is shaped when wet and then baked hard in an oven.

4 Artists paint pictures on a _ A _ V _ _.
5 If you want to knit something all you need is a pair of needles and some _ _ O _.
6 Most of Henry Moore's sculptures are carved out of S _ _ _ E.
7 If you want to make a lot of identical ornaments, make a mould and fill it with _ L _ _ T _ _. When this is dry and hard, you can paint it.
8 You can paint with many different kinds of _ _ I _ _ ; watercolours, oils and acrylics.

4 Phrasal verbs

A In Units 2 and 3 of the Student's Book, several meanings of the phrasal verbs *put on*, *put off*, and *put up* are covered. See how many you can remember. Write the correct phrasal verb next to each meaning.

1 increase   _____
2 distract   _____
3 discourage   _____
4 get dressed in, wear   _____
5 provide accommodation for   _____
6 build   _____
7 switch on   _____
8 postpone, delay   _____

B Fill the blanks in these sentences with an appropriate particle.

1 Never put _____ till tomorrow what you can do today!
2 Even though she put _____ every heater in the house, it was still freezing cold.
3 A lot of the tower blocks which were put _____ in the Sixties have been pulled down.
4 As soon as John got home, he took off his boots, put _____ his slippers and settled down to read the paper.
5 I'm sure that if they put _____ the price of cigarettes, more people would stop smoking.
6 Don't be put _____ by the colour! It tastes really nice!
7 You needn't look for a hotel when you come to the States. We can easily put you _____.
8 Could you turn down the radio a bit please? I'm trying to concentrate and the music is really putting me _____.

Writing

Articles ➤ Student's Book, page 46

A The following sentences A–J form an article on the topic of arts and crafts. Put them in the correct order and then divide the article into four paragraphs. The first sentence is given.

Coming down to earth

a   Are artists born or made? I've often wondered. 1

b   Then when I was a teenager, I decided to be more realistic.

c   I imagined myself living in an attic room in Paris painting masterpieces.

d   Giving someone a sweater which goes down to their knees, I discovered, is a sure way of ending any relationship.

e   In the end I was forced to admit that not everyone is born to be artistic.

f   I decided to take up knitting and from the age of sixteen I knitted a sweater for every boy I went out with.

g   Even when I was a child, I wanted to be an artist.

h   I don't really know why because, in my case, neither one nor the other seems to be true.

i   But the nearest I ever got to producing one was the painting-by-numbers Mona Lisa I did when I was twelve.

j   As a university student, I tried pottery but I wasn't any better at that.

B Write your own article about the best or worst thing you have ever made. Here are some ideas to get you started. Make brief notes.

- Mention the materials you used and describe how you made it. Did anything go wrong?
- Say how you felt when you'd finished it. What did people say about it?
- What did you do with it? What do you feel about it now?

Organize your ideas into three or four paragraphs. Then think of an appropriate title and opening sentence. Remember that your beginning should make people want to read your article.

Write your article in 120–180 words. Finally, check your grammar, spelling and punctuation.

EXAM TIP

Make sure you answer the question. If you don't, you will lose marks, even if your English is good.

4 Comparison

Reading

1 Before you read

You are going to read an article about a couple who left their children alone at home over Christmas. Why do you think they did this? Think of two or three possible explanations.

2 Reading

Now read the first paragraph of the article to find out if any of your explanations were right.

3 Comprehension

Choose from sentences A–G the one which fits each gap in the article. There is one sentence that does not fit anywhere.

A 'Who could ever think that as parents they would go away to enjoy themselves for 10 days?'

B As soon as the Schoos' plane landed, police boarded it and arrested them before they had unbuckled their seat-belts.

C In fact neither of the girls had made a long-distance phone call in their lives.

D The couple had pinned up a note in the kitchen telling the girls exactly what to wear on snowy days.

E According to one of the arresting officers, they didn't even inquire how their children were.

F She said they ran screaming and barefoot through the snow to her house.

G They had left a fully-stocked refrigerator, but they had not given their children an emergency telephone contact in Acapulco.

EXAM TIP

Read the text quickly before trying to fill the gaps, so that you get an idea of what it is about and what information is missing.

Couple abandon kids at Christmas

a To a chorus of angry shouts and insults, a wealthy Chicago couple have been charged with child cruelty after leaving their daughters, aged four and nine, alone at home while they spent Christmas on the beach at Acapulco, Mexico. David Schoo, aged 45 and his wife Sharon, aged 35, were handcuffed by waiting police, surrounded by reporters and insulted by onlookers after their return flight from Mexico landed at Chicago's O'Hare airport. The couple were immediately taken to jail where they will stay until their trial.

b Police said the daughters, Diana, aged 4 and Nicole, aged 9, had been left on their own in the Schoos' suburban Chicago home on December 20 when their parents set off for their 10-day holiday. [1] It also included a strict reminder to Diane and Nicole about the time they should go to bed. They even remembered to tell them when and where to leave the Christmas cookies for Santa Claus.

c There is clear evidence to show that the Schoos were quite determined to have an uninterrupted, trouble-free holiday, even if this meant neglecting their children. [2] The elder daughter Nicole

told a local television station, 'For a long time I felt really bad, wondering what they were doing and where they were.'

d 'How could anybody ever do this to their kids especially at Christmas time?' asked Connie Stadelmann, a neighbour. **3**

e Ms Stadelmann discovered the girls' plight on December 21 after the children accidentally set off a home fire alarm. **4** "I asked them where their mom and dad were. They said Mexico."

f The girls were looked after by another family while, unable to trace their parents, Chicago police were forced to monitor passenger lists on all flights from Mexico. **5**

g The sun-tanned couple were led through a crowd of reporters, but declined to comment. **6** The Schoos have been charged with child abandonment as well as cruelty.

h Reports compared the case with the comedy film *Home Alone*, in which a child is accidentally left behind by a Chicago family when they go on holiday to Europe. The film has a happy ending.

4 Vocabulary

A What or who do the words in italics in these extracts from the article refer to? The paragraph letters are given in brackets.
1 . . . while *they* spent Christmas on the beach . . . (a)
2 . . . had been left on *their* own . . . (b)
3 *They* even remembered to tell *them* when and where . . . (b)
4 How could anyone do *this* to their kids . . . (d)
5 . . . the comedy film *Home Alone,* in *which* a child is . . . (h)
6 . . . a Chicago family when *they* go on holiday to Europe. (h)

B Find words in the article which have these meanings. The paragraph letters are given in brackets.
1 rude or offensive words said to someone (a)
2 people who watch an event take place (a)
3 something to help someone to remember something (b)
4 proof that something has definitely happened (c)
5 difficult or unfortunate situation (e)
6 find what you are looking for (f)
7 refuse (g)
8 behaviour that deliberately causes pain or hardship (g)

C The text includes two American English words: *cookies* and *Mom*. In British English these are *biscuits* and *Mum*. Here are some more American English words. Match them with their British English equivalents a–i.

1	highway	a	handbag
2	sidewalk	b	petrol
3	subway	c	bill
4	elevator	d	pavement
5	rest room	e	underground
6	gas	f	main road
7	purse	g	public toilet
8	garbage can	h	dustbin
9	check (in restaurant)	i	lift

Vocabulary

1 Puzzle

This puzzle is made up of eleven 'relationship' words. Read the definitions and write the missing words.

Across

1 your superior at work
2 person you have a legal business relationship with
3 man engaged to be married to a woman
4 person who gives you work
5 person you give work to
6 person you work with
7 person you know but are not especially friendly with
8 female child
9 person who lives next door
10 man or boy's romantic partner

Down

11 your father's wife who is not your 'real' mother

2 Compound nouns

A Make compound nouns by matching a beginning with an ending. As you write the eight compound nouns, decide whether they are written as two words, e.g. *soap opera*, as two words joined by a hyphen, e.g. *self-confidence*, or as one word, e.g. *weekend*. An example is given.

	Beginning	Ending	Compound noun
1	back	site	*backpack*
2	front	work	_____
3	lunch	rise	_____
4	light	pack	_____
5	house	case	_____
6	price	time	_____
7	camp	page	_____
8	suit	house	_____

B Now choose the correct meaning from a–h for each of the compound nouns you have written.

a increase in cost
b first part of a newspaper
c midday meal period
d luggage for large things
e tower with flashing lamp to guide ships
f place to put up a tent
g large bag used by cyclists or walkers
h washing-up and hoovering are examples of this

3 Use of English

Read the text and decide which word, A, B, C, or D best fits each space. An example is given.

A daughter's story

My father died when I was very small, so there was always just my mother and I. Sometimes I used to wish that I had a brother or sister, not so much for someone to play with, but to take some of the (0) *pressure* of my mother's expectations off me.

My father had been in the Army, and apart from a small (1)_____ we were quite poor at first. But my mother (2)_____ as a teacher and managed to get herself a fairly well-paid post at a girls' private school. We must have had enough to (3)_____ on, but somehow money always remained a major topic of (4)_____. I remember sometimes feeling (5)_____ for eating because she worked so hard to (6)_____ our food. Apart from teaching at school, she used to give private (7)_____ and she also had a part-time job in a local library.

By the time I was eight I already knew she wanted me to be a lawyer or a doctor. It never (8)_____ to me to say no, or to wonder what I would really like to do. I would have been too (9)_____ of hurting her. I felt I owed it to her to make her proud of me.

When I was about 16, a man she knew became very (10)_____ in her. I liked him and thought it would be great if they got married. My mother would be happy, and she wouldn't have to work so hard and worry all the time. I could (11)_____ she liked him too, but she wouldn't hear of marrying him. She said she couldn't because of her responsibilities to me. I felt utterly miserable.

I worked terribly hard at college and actually (12)_____ to get a first class degree in law. I remember feeling a sense of relief that I had finally given her what she wanted. But it was all done for her, not me.

Two years later I married John, a barrister. My mother adored him. But it was around this time that I began to realize how (13)_____ I was with not having taken any of my own decisions about my life. Eventually, John and I (14)_____ up and I decided to switch careers and become a social worker. I had never seen my mother so upset. It was as if I had destroyed her life. We had an absolutely (15)_____ row and we have never been close since.

0	A tension	8	A occurred
	B pressure		B happened
	C demand		C thought
	D pain		D appeared
1	A grant	9	A anxious
	B fee		B shy
	C wage		C scared
	D pension		D concerned
2	A trained	10	A keen
	B learnt		B fond
	C taught		C interested
	D educated		D enthusiastic
3	A get	11	A tell
	B get by		B realize
	C pass by		C understand
	D go		D know
4	A comment	12	A succeeded
	B remark		B achieved
	C speech		C could
	D conversation		D managed
5	A guilty	13	A unusual
	B bad		B unhappy
	C embarrassed		C ungrateful
	D worried		D unfair
6	A serve	14	A separated
	B produce		B split
	C satisfy		C divorced
	D provide		D divided
7	A teaching	15	A angry
	B lessons		B cross
	C education		C furious
	D learning		D annoyed

4 Phrasal verbs

A Fill the gaps in these sentences with *up* or *down*.

1 If you don't hurry _____ you'll miss your train.

2 I think I've got flu – I probably picked it _____ while I was on holiday.

3 After the accident the policeman took _____ everything the driver said.

4 Because of the bad weather the plane touched _____ over an hour late.

5 I grew _____ in a little village just outside Edinburgh.

6 When I was 17 I took _____ scuba diving.

7 Can you put me _____ for the night? All the hotels are full.

8 He did all kinds of jobs in several different countries before he finally settled _____.

B Read each sentence, thinking carefully about the meaning of the phrasal verb in *italics*. Then decide whether each sentence is true or false.

1 If you *take to* something, it means you dislike it from the beginning.

2 If you want to save money you should *put* all the lights *on*.

3 University students in Britain usually *break up* for their summer holidays in June.

4 When water freezes, it *turns into* ice.

5 Another way of saying the meeting ended is to say that the meeting *broke up*.

6 We had *got through* all our money, so we went shopping and spent over £100.

7 If it's as important as you say, I'd better *put off* doing it until tomorrow.

8 You really *take after* your grandfather. You look exactly like him.

Grammar

1 Use of English

Most of the lines in this text contain an unnecessary word. A few of the lines are correct. Read the text carefully, find the extra words and mark them. Tick any lines that are correct. Two examples are given.

My favourite TV programmes

 0 First of all, I must <u>to</u> say that I don't watch much television.
00 This is because I've always got so many other things to do. ✓
 1 My two most favourite programmes are *Hard Rock* and
 2 *Open Air* – I try not to miss to them. *Hard Rock* is on every
 3 Friday night from 9 to 11 and usually has the brilliant rock
 4 bands playing live. They interview the bands, who are talk
 5 about music, their future plans and how they started playing.
 6 *Open Air* is completely different – it's for a magazine
 7 programme about the environment. It's on every Sunday
 8 evening at 7.30. Each week they investigate into an issue
 9 which is connected in some way with the environment. Last
10 week they have looked into pollution, and next week they're
11 interviewing with the president of Friends of the Earth.
12 There are a lots of people who watch television every night.
13 There are being so many programmes to choose from that
14 they can always find something that interesting. I don't
15 know why they do it – I think of most TV is just a waste of time.

2 Comparative adjectives and adverbs

➤ Grammar reference, Student's Book, page 202

Fill the gaps in 1–8 with the comparative form of a word from the list. You may have to change an adjective into an adverb. There are two more words than you need.

bad   far   fast   friendly   good   hard   hot   informal   simple   slow

1 I didn't realize you lived so near to the city centre. I thought you lived much _____ out.
2 My exam result was really disappointing. I thought it would have been _____ than that.
3 People used to wear smart clothes for work. These days everyone dresses _____.
4 British people have got a reputation for being cold and reserved, so I found them much _____ than I'd expected.

5 He says he's doing his best, but if you ask me, he could work a lot _____.
6 It was 39 degrees in London yesterday. That's even _____ than it was on Monday.
7 You're making the problem _____ than it really is. There must be a solution.
8 If you can't run _____ than that, you're going to miss the train.

3 Use of English

Complete the second sentence so that it has a similar meaning to the first sentence. Use up to five words including the word you are given. Do not change this word. An example is given.

1 Reading helps to improve your vocabulary. **more**
The _____ the better your vocabulary will be.
2 I really enjoyed my holiday. I can't wait to go back to Florida again. **enjoyable**
I had such _____ I can't wait to go back to Florida again.
3 He asked me when I wanted to start my new job and I said as soon as possible. **the**
He asked me when I wanted to start my new job and I said _____ better.
4 Computers used to be more expensive than they are now. **less**
Computers _____ now than they used to be.
5 Driving on motorways has become increasingly dangerous over the last 25 years. **and**
Driving on motorways has become _____ over the last 25 years.
6 I'm surprised there were such a lot of people at the match. **so**
It's _____ people at the match.
7 Yesterday was warm – it was 25 degrees. Today it's 27 degrees. **bit**
Today it's _____ it was yesterday.
8 City centres are more dangerous than they were 20 years ago. **safe**
City centres are not _____ they were 20 years ago.

EXAM TIP

Try to work out what grammatical structure you are being expected to use in each transformation.

Writing

Transactional letters ➤ Student's Book, page 54

A Read this jumbled letter asking for information about holidays in Scotland and work out the correct order of paragraphs A–E.

Then decide which of the small advertisements you think the letter is a reply to.

SCOTLAND

SELF CATERING SCOTLAND
'CONSULT THE EXPERTS'

0131 559 2389 24 hrs

Brodie's agency

Over 2,000 self-catering properies in all areas from luxury houses to croft cottages. Write or phone for brochure.

KINTYRE. 6 Cottages by sea. Slp 2-12. Farm, beach, boats, fishing. Tel 018806 8439

ISLE OF IONA, Argyll. Logan Hotel offers peaceful Hebridean holiday on this tiny island with superb views and lovely beaches; home cooking. Children welcome. Brochure: 016817 1082

HIGHLANDS Holiday cottages/ chalets. Individually situated. Contact M.McHugh. Tel 01463 9463095

COSY COTTAGES in far N-West. Choice of remote sandy bay or quiet coastal village. Lochs, mountains, beaches. Tel 01732 973204

HOLDEN COTTAGES. Quality s/c cottages in lovely locations throughout Scotland. Family run business. BOX 345

SCOTLAND HOLIDAY COTTAGES Ltd 300 properties in all areas. Col brochure. Tel 01234 965402

SCOTLAND SPECIALISTS Over 450 s/cat cottages. Scottish Country Breaks 0131 363 4590

A

Another consideration is the area. According to your advert, you have cottages in various parts of North-west Scotland. We would prefer the mountains, but would consider a village on the coast.

B

Please could you also let us have details of your prices. Are there reductions for teenagers and children of the ages I have mentioned?

C

I have just read your advertisement in an English-language newspaper published in my country, and I am now writing for further details of your accommodation.

D

We still have to make other arrangements, so please could you send this information as soon as possible.

E

First of all, our group will consist of five people: two adults, two teenagers, aged 16 and 14 and a child of nearly four. This means we will need a cottage with at least two bedrooms. We are interested in a holiday in the first week of June and would be most grateful if you could let us know whether you have a suitable cottage at this time.

B Read the letter again carefully and answer these questions.

1 What is the main topic of each of the five paragraphs?
2 How does the writer ask for information? Underline any examples you find.
3 Which of these features of formal writing does the letter include?
   a long sentences
   b an impersonal tone
   c long verb forms
   d polite phrases
   e passive verbs
   f single word verbs (equivalents of phrasal verbs)

C You are now going to arrange a week's holiday in Scotland for yourself and your family.

Choose another of the small advertisements which looks interesting. Make notes about the type of accommodation you need. Here are some points to think about.

- Who is in your group? What are their ages?
- How many bedrooms do you need?
- What sort of building would you prefer?
- What sort of area would you prefer?
- Are there any particular facilities you need to ask about?
- When do you want to stay in the accommodation?
- What are the prices at this time?
- Are there any other questions you need to ask about something in the advertisement?

Work out a suitable paragraph plan for your letter. Then write your letter in 120–180 words, referring to your notes and using the sample letter to help you. Finally, check your grammar, spelling and punctuation.

EXAM TIP

Remember to think about how formal or informal your letter should be.

Revision

This section gives you extra practice in the grammar and vocabulary covered in Units 1–4. Before you begin, remind yourself of this language by looking at the Student's Book units and the reference sections.
➤ Grammar reference, pages 200–204
➤ Vocabulary reference, pages 215–216

Grammar

1 Correct forms

Choose the correct form from the two choices given.
1 I keep *to lose / losing* my keys.
2 When I was young I used *to have / having* terrible nightmares.
3 It's getting rather late. *Shall / Will* I phone for a taxi?
4 It can hurt your eyes if you look directly at *a / the* sun.
5 Did you see *a / the* news on TV last night?
6 My car's broken down, so I'll have to get used to *walk / walking* everywhere.
7 Please stop *to worry / worrying* about me. I'm old enough to look after myself.
8 I can't help *to wish / wishing* I hadn't bought such an expensive watch.
9 My hair is nearly *so / as* long as yours.
10 They were playing *so / such* loud music at the party next door that I went round to complain.

2 Verb tenses

Fill the gaps in these sentences with the correct form of the verb in brackets.
1 Whenever John _____(drink) coffee, he gets a headache.
2 My birthday's next Tuesday. I _____(be) eighteen.
3 When John finishes university he _____ (work) abroad for a couple of years. At least that's his plan.
4 You've got enough to do. I _____(do) the shopping this week.
5 You'd better be quick. The train _____(leave) in five minutes.

6 I'm really annoyed with Helen. She is always _____(criticize) me.
7 This year we _____(spend) Christmas in Australia. We've already booked our flight.
8 On July 26 next year, my parents _____(live) in this house for exactly 25 years.
9 This time tomorrow you _____(do) your English exam. There'll still be half an hour left.
10 When I was fifteen, I usually _____(go) to school by bus.

3 Key word transformations

Complete the second sentence using the word given.
1 It was such a cold day yesterday that I wore my winter coat. **so**
   Yesterday it _____ that I wore my winter coat.
2 After a hard day's work, he usually falls asleep on the train. **tends**
   After a hard day's work _____ , asleep on the train.
3 As he became more famous, it was more difficult for him to avoid newspaper reporters. **the**
   The more famous he became, _____ for him to avoid newspaper reporters.
4 My last exam is on Thursday afternoon. **finished**
   By Friday morning I _____ my exams.
5 I'm on the point of losing my temper! **about**
   I'm _____ my temper.
6 I'm sorry I sent you that letter. It was very rude of me. **regret**
   I _____ . It was very rude of me.
7 When I was a child we lived in Bristol. **used**
   We _____ when I was a child.
8 Our house is older than all the other houses in the road. **the**
   Our house is _____ in the road.

9 An old motorbike was stolen from the car park. A teenage boy stole it. **responsible**

A teenage boy is _____ an old motorbike from the car park.

10 It was two years ago at the end of this week that I started working here. **been**

At the end of this week I _____ here for two years.

Vocabulary

1 Definitions

Match these words with their definitions. There are two more words than you need.

acquaintance audience   basement   colleague
channel   clay   common sense community
detached   interval   lightning   recluse
stress

1 used to describe a house which is not joined to another house on either side
2 a person you know but are not particularly friendly with
3 tension caused by worrying too much or by working too hard
4 a group of people who attend a concert or show
5 a short break between two parts of a film or play
6 a room in a building that is below ground level
7 a sudden bright flash in the sky during a thunderstorm
8 natural intelligence; the ability to make good decisions
9 a television or radio station
10 a substance that is used to make pottery (bowls, plates, etc.)

2 Word building

Complete the table with words related to those given.

noun	verb
1 improvement	_____
2 _____	expect
3 management	_____
4 _____	perform
5 _____	educate
6 resident	_____
7 _____	marry
8 decision	_____
9 _____	amaze
10 applause	_____

3 Phrasal verbs

A Match these phrasal verbs (1–10) with their meanings (a–j). Use each meaning once only.

1 get through   a start doing
2 go on   b catch (a disease)
3 grow up   c increase
4 pick up   d make something start to work
5 put off   e discourage
6 put on   f spend
7 put up   g begin to live a routine life
8 settle down   h develop into an adult
9 take up   i become
10 turn into   j take place

B Now fill the gaps in the sentences below with the correct form of one of the phrasal verbs in 3A.

1 The thought of the long flight has always _____ me _____ going to Australia.
2 I've had this cold for nearly two weeks and I've no idea where I _____ it _____.
3 He travelled all over the world before he finally _____ and got a normal 9–5 job.
4 Every year the government _____ the price of cigarettes.
5 My father was born and _____ in the far north of Scotland.
6 When it's rainy or foggy it's sensible to _____ your car headlights.
7 As a child, my brother was really naughty, but he has _____ a perfectly normal adult.
8 By the second day of our holiday we had _____ over half our pocket money.
9 If you want to get fit, why don't you _____ walking or aerobics?
10 I wonder where all those people are going? Perhaps something _____ in the town centre.

You are now ready to do Progress test 1.

5 Narrative

Reading

1 Before you read

You are going to read an article about world records in athletics. First, decide if you think these statements are true or false.

1 Athletes of the future will be taller and stronger than today's athletes are.
2 In the future, drug-taking in sports will be legalized.
3 What athletes eat and drink before a race is more important than what they eat and drink after a race.
4 A good running shoe helps athletes run faster.
5 The most important factor in long jumping is the speed of the approach.

2 Reading

Read the article quickly to get an idea of what it is about and to check your answers to 1 above.

3 Comprehension

Choose the most appropriate heading from the list A–H for each part (1–6) of the article. There is one extra heading which you do not need to use.
An example is given.

A Research holds the key to success
B New and improved techniques
C A new kind of athlete
D New equipment has made a difference
E Athletes are what they eat
F Personalized programmes will help
G The influence of drugs
H Is there a limit to record-breaking?

EXAM TIP

As you read the text section by section underline any words which go with the headings.

RECORD-BREAKERS

0   H

A world record is every athlete's dream, but the hard-won records of a few years ago are mostly just
5   today's qualifying times. Roger Bannister's famous four-minute mile of 1956 has been beaten by nearly 15 seconds, while almost an
10   hour and twenty minutes has been taken off the women's marathon since 1953. 'Faster, higher, stronger', is the Olympic motto, and today's
15   competitors continue to push back the boundaries of what the body can achieve. But one wonders if this can continue.

1

The last forty years have seen many important
20   technological advances. For example, since the introduction of strong, flexible fibreglass poles, over a metre has been added to the pole vault record. There have also been important developments in the design of the running shoe. And while a shoe
25   won't actually make someone run faster, modern shoes do mean many more miles of comfortable, injury-free training.

2

Pushing back the limits now depends more on science, technology and medicine than anything
30   else. Athletic technique, training programmes and diets are all being studied to find ways of taking a few more seconds off or adding a few more centimetres to that elusive world record. It seems that natural ability and hard work are no longer enough.

3

35   The search to find more efficient ways of moving goes on. Analysis of an athlete's style is particularly useful for events like jumping and throwing. Studies show that long jumpers need to concentrate not on the speed of approach, as once thought, but on the
40   angle their bodies make with the ground as they

take off. However, the rules governing each sport limit advances achieved by new styles. For instance only one-footed take-offs are allowed in the high jump.

4

In the future, it should be possible to develop a
45 more individual approach to training programmes. Athletes will keep detailed diaries and collect data to help predict the point when training becomes overtraining, the cause of many injuries. If athletes feed all their information into a database, it may
50 then be possible to predict patterns and to advise them individually when they should cut down.

5

Combining the right diet with a training programme is vital. Athletes are continually searching for that special 'go-faster' ingredient, but apparently it's
55 still a battle to get them to drink sufficient liquid and to follow a balanced healthy diet throughout all phases of training, competition and recovery. Diet in the period after an event is particularly important and often neglected. An athlete who doesn't
60 replace all the liquid lost immediately after a hard run won't be able to repeat the performance at the same level 24 hours later.

6

So what of the future? It is no
65 secret that many records are not authentic and with the tightening of drugs controls,
70 performances may actually decline, particularly in events like the shot putt and discus. The throwers
75 of the future will be 'clean' and smaller and will pay more attention to technique and less
80 to strength.

4 Vocabulary

A Match these words from the article with the meanings a–h below.
1 motto (line 14)
2 flexible (line 21)
3 elusive (line 33)
4 predict (line 47)
5 vital (line 53)
6 battle (line 55)
7 neglect (line 59)
8 authentic (line 67)

a pay too little or no attention to
b say what will happen
c able to bend easily without breaking
d genuine
e struggle, fight
f difficult to find, achieve
g essential
h saying used as a guide to behaviour

B Now fill each gap in these sentences with one of the words above, changing the form of the word if necessary.

1 Getting to work in the rush hour can be a bit of a _____.
2 Babies have extremely _____ bodies.
3 We thought the painting was a fake but it turned out to be _____ after all.
4 The weather forecaster _____ sunshine and showers for tomorrow.
5 When people are depressed they often _____ their appearance.
6 Our school _____ was 'Nothing but the best'.
7 It's absolutely _____ to read any legal document extremely carefully before you sign it.
8 Happiness is an _____ quality.

Grammar

1 Past tenses

➤ Grammar reference, Student's Book, page 204

A Fill the gaps in this story with a verb from the box below. Use an appropriate past tense and make any other changes that are necessary.

ask	be	begin	drive	drive off
get in	give	have	leave	make
notice	open	pick up	rain	reach
realize	see	shake	try	wait

The Mysterious Hitchhiker

A young woman (1)_____ through lonely countryside. It (2)_____ heavily and it (3)_____ to get dark. Suddenly she (4)_____ an old woman by the side of the road, holding her hand out as if she wanted a lift. 'I can't leave her out in this weather,' the young woman said to herself. So she stopped the car and (5)_____ the door. 'Do you want a lift?' she (6)_____. The old woman nodded and (7)_____.

As she (8)_____ herself comfortable, the young woman asked her, '(9)_____ you _____ long?' The old woman (10)_____ her head. 'You were lucky then,' the young woman commented, wondering why the old woman never spoke. She (11)_____ again. 'Nasty weather for the time of year,' she continued. The old woman nodded in agreement. No matter what the young woman said the hitchhiker (12)_____ no answer except for a nod or a shake of the head.

All of a sudden, the young woman (13)_____ that her passenger's hands were very large and hairy. With a shock she (14)_____ that the hitchhiker wasn't an old woman at all but a man dressed up as an old woman. She braked suddenly. 'I can't see out of the rear window,' she explained. 'Would you mind cleaning it for me?' The hitchhiker nodded and opened the car door. As soon as the hitchhiker (15)_____ out of the car, the terrified woman (16)_____ at top speed.

When she (17)_____ the next village she stopped. She noticed that the hitchhiker (18)_____ a handbag behind. She (19)_____ it _____ and opened it. Inside the bag was a gun. She (20)_____ a narrow escape!

B Put the verbs in brackets in these sentences into an appropriate past tense. Choose from past simple, past continuous, present perfect simple, present perfect continuous or past perfect simple. Make any other changes that are necessary. Sometimes there is more than one possible answer.

1 Jan _____ (go) to live in Italy in 1992. She _____ (not be) in the country long before she _____ (fall) in love and _____ (get married).

2 '_____ (not finish) your homework yet Alex? You _____ (do) it for ages.'
'I _____ (do) most of it but I'm stuck on the last bit.'

3 I know I _____ (say) I'd phone you as soon as I _____ (get back) but I _____ (not can) remember where I _____ (write down) your new number.

4 It's typical, isn't it! I _____ just _____ (put) shampoo on my hair when the phone _____ (ring). I _____ (think) it might be important so I _____ (rush) downstairs. Needless to say, it _____ (stop) ringing before I _____ (reach) it.

5 'I'm terribly sorry but I _____ (forget) your name.'

6 Police say that the man they wish to question _____ (have) long hair and _____ (wear) a denim jacket and jeans. He _____ (drive off) in a stolen car.

7 Julie _____ just _____ (cover) herself in sun tan lotion when the sun _____ (go) behind a large black cloud.

8 I _____ (think) of calling Sam and _____ just _____ (pick up) my address book to look up her number when the phone _____ (start) ringing. It _____ (be) her!

9 'Is anything the matter?'
'No. I _____ (peel) onions. Onions always make me cry.'

10 I _____ (sit) on the bus on my way to work when I _____ (realize; leave) something cooking on the stove.

2 Use of English

A Read through the article quickly. Is it about a new sport or an old sport which has been revived? How did you decide?

B Read the article again and fill each gap with one suitable word. An example is given.

Do you need a change? Are you fed up (0) ___with___ horse-racing? Tired (1)_____ watching dogs race round a track? If you are, then what you need (2)_____ try is sheep-racing.

Sheep-racing, which started (3)_____ a joke, was the idea of Richard Turner, a farmer in the south of England. Much to his surprise (4)_____ caught on and the races are now (5)_____ a success that Richard (6)_____ to organize one every day.

A race consists of six sheep running round a 240 metre track. The sheep have funny names (7)_____ 'Little Pullover' and (8)_____ ridden by woollen jockeys, (9)_____ sometimes fall off.

Rather surprisingly the sheep are (10)_____ to move fast – the course record is 22 seconds. But (11)_____ makes these lazy creatures move (12)_____ quickly? The answer is greed. Food (13)_____ put at the finish.

Like horse-racing (14)_____ dog-racing, people bet on which sheep (15)_____ be the winner. The difference here is that all profits go to the local hospital.

Vocabulary

1 Use of English

Read through this text. Then use the word in capital letters to form a word which fits in the gap. An example is given.

A man was extremely (0)_*fortunate*_ to suffer only minor (1)_____ after falling 1,000 metres from a small aircraft yesterday.

Thrown out of the plane when he (2)_____ touched a wrong button, his situation was worsened by the (3)_____ of his parachute to open properly. (4)_____ Des Maloney had a soft (5)_____ in a field near Colchester, Essex.

Although it was his first (6)_____ in this particular plane, Des Maloney is not an (7)_____ pilot: he has flown for five years.

There is to be an immediate (8)_____ into the incident. The plane had recently passed a (9)_____ examination. Des, meantime, following an (10) _____ reunion with his brother, Tom, is planning a big celebration.

0	FORTUNE	6	FLY
1	INJURE	7	EXPERIENCE
2	ACCIDENT	8	INVESTIGATE
3	FAIL	9	SAFE
4	LUCK	10	EMOTION
5	LAND		

EXAM TIP

Don't forget that you may have to make more than one change to the word given. Check whether a negative is required.

2 Topic vocabulary

➤ Vocabulary reference, Student's Book, page 216

Which sports are these people talking about?

1 A lot of people think it should be banned. You need to be physically very tough and have very quick reflexes. You don't need any equipment; just a pair of gloves and some lace-up boots. _____

2 This is a fast, fairly aggressive team game and it is played indoors on a rink. You need a pair of skates and a stick. You also need to be a good skater and have very fast reflexes. _____

3 This is mainly a man's sport. You have to be very strong and muscular, and have good balance. You have to rub powder on your hands before lifting to stop your hands slipping. _____

4 It's usually played as an individual sport. The equipment can be quite expensive. You need a set of clubs and lots of balls as you tend to lose quite a few. _____

3 Crossword

➤ Vocabulary reference, Student's Book, page 216

Read the clues and complete this crossword.

Across

1 (and 2 down) You need one of these for Formula One events. (6, 3)
6 A serve in tennis that is so good the other player cannot return it. (3)
7 In football you _____ a goal. (5)
8 You have to hit the ball over this in tennis. (3)
11 The number of players in a football side, excluding the goalkeeper. (3)
12 A competition in which people run to see who is the fastest. (4)
14 In hockey you use this to hit the ball. (5)
15 If you do 12 down, you will need this to sit on. (6)
16 To start play by throwing a shuttlecock into the air and hitting it. (5)

Down

1 You need this to play tennis, badminton or squash. (6)
2 See 1 across. (3)
3 What you do at a rink. (8)
4 In hockey you hit the ball into this area to get points. (4)
5 The person who controls a football match. (7)

8 In some sports this means a score of no points. (3)
9 Groups of people who play against each other. (5)
10 To try to take the ball from another player in football or hockey. (6)
12 You _____ a horse. (Note: the letters are jumbled) (4)
13 To kick the ball to another player in football. (4)

4 Phrasal verbs

Fill the gaps in these sentences with an appropriate particle.

1 If you drop me _____ on the corner, I can walk the rest of the way.

2 Why don't you take _____ your coat and make yourself comfortable?

3 I was woken _____ by a rumble of thunder directly overhead.

4 'Could you give me a lift to the airport tomorrow?' 'Sure. I'll pick you _____ around 7.'

5 If we set _____ early, we'll miss the rush.

6 Don't throw _____ your glass bottles. Recycle them.

7 I haven't looked forward _____ a holiday so much in years.

Writing

Stories ➤ Student's Book, page 68

A Divide this text into three paragraphs and add all the necessary punctuation. You can check how direct speech is punctuated in the Grammar reference in the Student's Book on page 199.

an embarrassing incident

one summer job i had as a student was in a rather exclusive restaurant in glasgow on this particular day we were expecting forty members of a football team for lunch i was given the job of peeling the potatoes i thought i was managing quite well with my small knife until the owner appeared to see how i was getting on she was amazed that i was using a knife and asked why i wasnt using the potato peeler i had no idea what a potato peeler was so she led me into a small room behind the main kitchen there on the table was a small machine rather like the rubbish bins some people have in their bathrooms she explained as if to a small child that i had to put the potatoes in close the lid and press the button when she came back ten minutes later i told her i thought it was quicker to do them by hand she asked what i meant well they arent ready yet i replied you can imagine how i felt when she lifted the lid and took out the potatoes the size of peas the potato peeler was not automatic

B The following story has been jumbled up. There should be three paragraphs, each of which has an opening sentence and three other sentences. The opening sentences are given below. Decide which other sentences (a–i) belong to each paragraph. Then put the sentences in order. An example is given.

Paragraph 1
Disaster struck a couple of days before Tessa's departure when she fell and broke her arm.

_____ c _____   _____   _____

Paragraph 2
The budgie, however, turned out to be the main problem.

_____   _____   _____

Paragraph 3
Two hours later the plane landed and she got off.

_____   _____   _____

a	It was then that Tessa started to worry.
b	She couldn't believe her luck when she heard the sound of a pneumatic drill: the noise drowned everything.
c	She was in Spain when it happened but was returning to Britain for Christmas.
d	Relieved, she walked unchecked through Customs but made up her mind never to do it again.
e	She knew that it was illegal to take animals into Britain without declaring them, but she hadn't thought what would happen if she was caught.
f	Unfortunately, she had already bought presents for everyone at home as well as a *budgie for her aunt.
g	It protested loudly from its cardboard box beneath her seat causing passengers nearby to turn round.
h	The budgie was still making a lot of noise and she was shaking as she walked towards Customs.
i	Carrying everything was now going to be extremely difficult.

*budgie – a small, brightly-coloured bird often kept as a pet

C Write a story about someone who did something wrong. Your story can be true or imaginary but you must begin or end it with the words *Never again*. Use the paragraph plan and the ideas below to help you.

Paragraph 1   Set the scene. Who? When? Where?
Paragraph 2   What happened?
Paragraph 3   How did the story end?

Write your story in 120–180 words. Finally, check your grammar, spelling and punctuation.

EXAM TIP ─────────────────

Don't write about too many events. It's better to describe fewer things in more detail.

6 Conditions

Reading

1 Before you read

Look at the title of the article and decide whether it is about
1 a young woman becoming a criminal
2 a young woman finding a new home
3 a young woman being kidnapped by terrorists.

2 Reading

Read the main part of the article quickly to find out if you were right. Don't read the missing paragraphs yet.

3 Comprehension

Read the missing paragraphs A–G and decide where each one fits in the article. Remember there is one more paragraph than you need.

A Although we had been preparing for her return this autumn, the whole family has been in confusion. She is closer than ever to her American family. She still loves us, but we are no longer her primary family and knowing this is terrible.

B Recently I spoke to her on the phone, trying to understand the college arrangements there. She sounds confused. Her employers did not inform us they were taking on this parental responsibility and that is worrying.

C This family has broken so many rules of the au pair scheme that I could have my daughter returned home. But that would only make her hate us. I feel that somewhere she has lost her own identity, but all we can do is to keep in touch with her, to keep telling her we love her and that she will always have a home here.

D As we said our goodbyes, she was excited but nervous. For an 18-year-old who had rarely been away from home, this was an enormous step.

E We had always been a close family, but I wouldn't say that we had been harsh or particularly possessive parents. We just wanted to see our children grow up to be happy.

F This is more than just the pain of losing the child we love. Many inexperienced 18-year-olds suffer culture shock when they return home after a year of exciting living. Yet no-one warns them or their parents about this, and many of them take several months to settle again.

Somebody's stolen my daughter

Three years ago, my daughter took her exams, won a university place and decided to take a year off between leaving school and starting university. She chose to go to America as an au pair and we saw her off at the airport in August.

1

'Promise me Granny will still be alive when I get home,' she said seriously as she was about to board her plane. Then my 10-year-old daughter said what I was thinking secretly : 'We might never see her again,' she said sadly.

2

She returned for university, but she was different. She reacted badly to being back. She was cold, hostile and treated us as strangers. She cried over photographs of the children she had cared for in

America, but made hardly any contact with us. Then, in her summer term, she rang to say that she was returning to America, where she felt she belonged. After a painful summer, she returned to the US.

3

Now she has found a way to stay there: her employers are paying for her to go to college. She will live and work with them in return for the fees. I feel they have bought her.

4

With our daughter it has been even more serious. She was so good at her job that her employers took a holiday, leaving her alone with three children under three; so good that during the year she was back here, they kept asking her to return,

saying 'We wish you would become a permanent member of our family.'

5

Maybe worrying is an understatement. Last week I felt that my daughter wanted to say something on the phone but she was too tired to express herself clearly. She was sure she wanted to stay in America. But then she said: 'I don't know. I feel I'm being persuaded by the family here.'

6

If she starts American college this autumn, she will be 25 when she finishes. She will miss her brother and sister growing up. I cannot imagine how this will end, but I would hesitate to recommend this particular au pair scheme to other parents of an inexperienced school-leaver.

G During that first year, I lived for her letters. At least she was happy; she had settled quickly and loved her American family. I had anxious moments, such as when she said that they were trying to persuade her to stay 'for ever'.

EXAM TIP

When deciding where the paragraphs should fit, think about the sequence of events or ideas in the text.

4 Vocabulary

Find words or phrases in the article (including the missing paragraphs) which mean the same as 1–6.

1 to get on (an aircraft) _____

2 unfriendly _____

3 worried, uneasy _____

4 most important, first _____

5 feeling of confusion when living in another country _____

6 fixed, long-term _____

Grammar

1 Conditional sentences

➤ Grammar reference, Student's Book, page 205

A Complete these conditional sentences using the correct form of the verb in brackets.

1 If we're home early tonight, we _____ (go) swimming with you.

2 If Paul drinks coffee at night, it _____ (take) him ages to get to sleep.

3 If Anna hung her clothes up, her room _____ (look) so untidy.

4 If I see your father in the next hour, I _____ (tell) him you're looking for him.

5 If Andrew hadn't been so rude, his colleagues _____ (stop) talking to him.

6 My mother never gives people lifts in her car if she _____ (be) on her own.

7 The car seat _____ (get) wet, if you had closed the window.

8 My grandfather can't see very well if he _____ (have got) his glasses on.

9 I _____ (phone) you if I can't get there.

10 You'd be better at tennis if you _____ (practise) more regularly.

B Rewrite 1–8 as Type 2 or 3 conditional sentences.

Example: He's tired because he works all the time.
If he didn't work all the time, he wouldn't be tired.

1 Sue was ill, so she didn't go to the party.

_____

2 I don't go to the theatre very often because there isn't one in my town.

_____

3 Jeff didn't play football because he'd broken his leg.

_____

4 My mother never goes swimming because she's afraid of water.

_____

5 Of course I'd like to buy a yacht but I haven't got £100,000 to spare.

_____

6 It didn't snow, so we couldn't go skiing.

_____

7 He walked into the road sign because he wasn't looking where he was going.

_____

8 I can't send her a postcard because I don't know her address.

_____

2 Use of English

Complete the second sentence so that it has a similar meaning to the first sentence. Use up to five words including the word you are given. Do not change this word. An example is given.

0 You won't know what to do if you don't read the instructions carefully. **unless**
You won't know what to do ___*unless you read*___ the instructions carefully.

1 I can't help you unless you tell me what the problem is. **if**
I can't help you _____ me what the problem is.

2 If you hadn't left the door unlocked, the thief wouldn't have got in so easily. **because**
The thief found it easy to get in _____ _____ the door unlocked.

3 I would have taken a photo of you, but I didn't bring my camera. **if**
I would have taken a photo of you _____ _____ my camera.

4 Whenever you are in our area, don't forget to call in. **if**
Remember _____ are in our area.

5 If I'd got a driving licence, I could drive your car. **so**
I haven't got a driving licence, _____ _____ your car.

6 If you hadn't been driving so fast, it's possible that the crash would not have been so serious. **might**
If you hadn't been driving so fast, the _____ _____ so serious.

7 The service in that restaurant won't improve if nobody ever complains. **unless**
_____, the service in that restaurant won't improve.

8 If we hurry, it's still possible for us to get to the cinema on time. **may**
If we hurry, _____ to the cinema on time.

3 Use of English

A As you read quickly through the article, decide which is the best description of Belinda.
1 She used to entertain visitors to London Zoo.
2 She was an extremely rare species of spider.
3 She was used to find out whether people were afraid of spiders.

B Read the article again and fill each gap with one suitable word. An example is given.

Belinda, the friendly spider, dies at 22

Belinda, a film and television starlet who worked all her life to help people with phobias, has died at the age of 22. To mark the occasion, London Zoo took (0) _the_ unusual step of issuing this obituary notice: 'Born (1)_____ Mexico, Belinda's poverty-to-riches career began after she arrived at the zoo in 1978 and her star quality and docile, friendly and outgoing character made (2)_____ a natural ambassador for the zoo.'

Belinda died childless. This is unusual (3)_____ a Mexican red-kneed, bird-eating spider. She responded well to people and people responded to her. 'She was a real character,' said Dave Clarke, senior keeper (4)_____ the zoo. 'We get very attached (5)_____ these creatures.'

Belinda, (6)_____ was around 17 cm wide and rather furry, kept her weight to 45 g (7)_____ eating a locust (8)_____ three weeks. She was best-known for appearing before arachnophobes, people with a terrible fear (9)_____ spiders. 'We work with hypnotists to cure people with arachnophobia,' said her keeper. 'People are told how nice spiders (10)_____ and then given hypnotherapy. After (11)_____ they come in to meet the spider. (12)_____ they are able to hold Belinda, (13)_____ means that they are cured of (14)_____ fear.'

Belinda's last starring role (15)_____ in the zoo's cinema and television advertising campaign. Bird-eating spiders from the zoo also appeared in films with Indiana Jones and James Bond.

Vocabulary

1 Body idioms

➤ Vocabulary reference, Student's Book, page 216

Choose the correct part of the body from the list to fill the gaps in the idioms in *italics* in these sentences. There are two more words than you need.

arm   back   feet   finger   hair   head   legs
neck   nose   tongue

1 Her father says 'Yes' to everything she asks for. She can *twist him round her little _____*.
2 I wouldn't get too friendly with John if I were you. He's quite likely to *stab you in the _____*.
3 I stayed up and watched the late horror film on TV last night. It really was frightening. It made *my _____ stand on end*.
4 By the time children are 16 or 17 they've learnt *to stand on their own two _____*.
5 I'd give *my right _____* for a ticket to the Olympic Games.
6 As usual I've got too much work to do, but I'm just about managing *to keep my _____ above water*.
7 The person sitting behind me was a real *pain in the _____*. He talked all the way through the film.
8 I can't remember her name – it's driving me mad – it's *on the tip of my _____*.

2 Phrasal verbs

A Replace the verbs in *italics* in sentences 1–6 with one of the phrasal verbs listed below. You do not need to use one of the verbs.

bump into   carry on   carry out   find out
give away   pass out   split up

1 Please let me know if you *discover* where she lives.
2 My sister and her husband *separated* last year.
3 It was so hot yesterday that three people *fainted* while they were waiting for the train.
4 *Continue* with what you were saying – it was really interesting.
5 I've decided that I'm not going to *reveal* any more information.
6 I've just *met* an old school friend that I haven't seen for years.

B Match the sentence beginnings 1–8 with endings a–h and fill the gaps in the endings with a suitable form of one of the phrasal verbs listed below.

1 My parents are expecting me to do really well in my exams

2 In spite of the work of environmentalists

3 My car's being repaired today

4 The company has just won a large new order from the USA

5 Only 20 students wanted to go on the trip to the theatre

6 I've looked everywhere for my glasses

7 We were held up for over 45 minutes in the rush hour traffic

8 No-one's sure what the people of the town think about the new road,

a so a colleague is _____ me _____ and taking me to work.

b so to _____ the numbers we invited their parents and friends as well.

c I just hope I don't _____ them _____.

d even though we'd _____ an hour earlier than usual.

e so I just hope they haven't been _____ by mistake.

f so they're going to _____ 50 extra workers.

g so the council are _____ a survey into people's attitudes.

h several species of animals will _____ in the next 50 years.

carry out	die out	let down	make up
pick up	set off	take on	throw away

3 Use of English

A Read this text about an American businessman, but don't fill the gaps until you have found the answers to these questions.

1 What kind of animal is mentioned in the text?

_____

2 What kind of vehicles are mentioned?

_____

B Now read the article again and fill the gaps with the most suitable word or phrase, A, B, C or D.

AN UNWANTED PASSENGER

An American businessman was on a trip to Asia. He decided to (1)_____ a few days off and see something of the countryside, so he hired a car.

At first everything (2)_____ perfectly, but suddenly the weather changed and he (3)_____ himself in the middle of a tropical storm. Driving became impossible, so he pulled into the side of the road and waited until the rain had stopped before (4)_____ again.

A few miles further on, as he was (5)_____ gear, he felt something smooth move across his wrist. He (6)_____ down and saw a large python slithering through a gap in the floor. He (7)_____ the brakes, wanting to get out, but the snake was too quick for him. Within seconds it had wrapped itself (8)_____ him squeezing the breath out of him.

The terrified businessman (9)_____ to get hold of the snake's head and tried to hit it against the window. But the snake was too strong and the man thought he was going to die.

Suddenly he heard the screech of tyres and saw a lorry (10)_____ alongside. The driver jumped out and shouted at him to let go of the snake. Instantly the other driver killed it with a knife. He then explained that the snake must have got in when the car had been parked.

1	A put	5	A changing	8	A over
	B go		B adapting		B round
	C take		C altering		C on
	D bring		D accelerating		D across
2	A felt	6	A saw	9	A succeeded
	B went		B noticed		B finished
	C was		C looked		C managed
	D passed		D watched		D achieved
3	A found	7	A put off	10	A pull out
	B saw		B got on		B bring up
	C situated		C took off		C end up
	D placed		D put on		D pull up
4	A driving off				
	B taking off				
	C pulling off				
	D making off				

EXAM TIP

Don't choose the first word which seems to fit. Some of the alternative answers are meant to mislead you.

Writing

Reports ➤ Student's Book, page 82

A This report is about traffic conditions in a British town. As you read it for the first time, choose suitable sub-headings for the sections 1–5 from A–G below. There are two extra sub-headings that you do not need to use. Don't worry about the gaps yet.

A Air quality
B The growth in traffic
C The problem in brief
D Financial considerations
E Recommendations
F Technical problems
G Road safety

TRAFFIC IN NEWCHESTER: the current situation

1

(1)_____ is to draw attention to the current traffic situation in our town. Public opinion surveys show that residents are becoming increasingly concerned about a wide range of problems associated directly and indirectly with traffic.

2

(2)_____, from simple observation, that the amount of traffic on our streets is increasing dramatically year by year. During rush hour periods, over 20,000 vehicles an hour now use the roads in and out of the town centre. (3)_____ it takes pedestrians nearly three minutes to cross the main street at these times.

3

It is also a fact that many drivers no longer observe the speed limit in operation in the town centre. (4)_____ that nearly half male drivers and over a quarter of female drivers go considerably faster than this. Accident figures are also increasing. In the first half of this year, serious accidents have gone up by nearly 20 per cent since the same period last year.

4

(5)_____ to many residents is the pollution caused by traffic. This summer an increasing number of people are complaining about stinging eyes and sore throats. (6)_____ that many of these symptoms are caused by the fumes from cars and buses.

5

(7)_____, the committee is making the following suggestions. Firstly, the council should provide cheap car parks on the outskirts of town and free bus services to the centre. Secondly, police should be given increased powers to deal with drivers who exceed the speed limit in the town centre. (8)_____, the air quality in the town should be checked carefully and regularly.

B Read the report again and fill each gap 1–8 with one of these phrases.
a After careful study
b Doctors have confirmed
c It is quite clear
d Lastly
e On average
f The police report
g The purpose of this report
h What is equally worrying

C Write a report about the traffic situation in your own town. Plan your report in the following stages.

• Think about the traffic situation in your own town or in a town you know well. If you have the opportunity, discuss your ideas with other students, friends or members of your family.
• Make brief notes of the points you want to include.
• Group your ideas into sections and think of sub-headings for each section. Choose a suitable title for your report.
• Decide on an order of importance for your report sections.
• Use your final section to offer some practical suggestions for dealing with any problems you have written about.
• Before you write, look at pages 82–83 of the Student's Book. You can also refer to the model report above for ideas.
• Write your report in 120–180 words. Most of the sections should be factual, but you may offer opinions in your last section.

EXAM TIP

Make sure the factual information you give is relevant to the topic of the report.

7 Description

Reading

1 Before you read

A Read this joke and try to answer the questions which follow.

'What do you say to a British university graduate with a job?'
'I don't know. What **do** you say to a British university graduate with a job?'
'Hamburger and chips, please.'

1 Where is the graduate working?
2 Why is the graduate working there?
3 What does the joke tell us about the job situation in Britain?

B You are going to read an article which gives young people advice on choosing a career and getting a good job. First, note down the advice that you would give.

_____

_____

_____

2 Reading

As you read the article for the first time see how many of your ideas are mentioned and tick them off.

3 Comprehension

Choose the most suitable heading from the list A–H for each part (1–6) of the article. There is one extra heading which you do not need to use. An example is given.
A Decide on a dream
B Be ambitious
C Get informed
D Sell yourself
E Get experience
F Be realistic
G Use your contacts
H Be positive

HOW TO GET THE JOB OF YOUR DREAMS

0 H

The main complaint from young people these days seems to be 'I don't know what I want to do' followed closely by 'It's pointless trying anyway.' Times have changed and the job market is not what it was with even graduates living off state unemployment benefits. But there is work if you want it, and if you are prepared to try hard and follow our handy and helpful plan for Getting The Job Of Your Dreams, you can still find your first foothold on the career ladder.

1

Compromise, improvise and give up your ideas of walking straight into a company director's job and you may well find that later rather than sooner you are engaged in doing a useful and rewarding job.

EXAM TIP

Remember that there is an extra heading which you do not need to use. Check that it doesn't fit anywhere in the text.

4 Vocabulary

Find words or phrases in the article with these meanings. The paragraph number is given in brackets.
a useless (0)
b accept less then you wanted (1)
c giving personal satisfaction and pleasure (1)
d difficult, awkward (3)
e contact (4)
f advantages and disadvantages (4)
g learned directly, not from books or other people (4)
h people you work with in a professional job (5)
i kind and caring (6)

Think about what you would like to do. If you hate children, forget about primary school teaching. If you can't stand writing, forget about journalism. Do you want to work abroad? Do you want to work in an office? Be imaginative! Don't limit yourself to what you want to be, but to what you like to do. And watching telly doesn't count!

3

If you like listening to people's problems and helping your friends out when they're in tricky situations, you should find out about the kind of jobs which involve this sort of work. Psychotherapy, social work, teaching, and personnel management are some of the jobs you could do. Find out what you would have to do in the job, and how you could get qualified.

4

Get in touch with people you know who already have your dream job. Ask to spend a day 'shadowing' them. They can explain how they got where they are today, the pros and cons, the salary and other details and you can get first-hand experience of what the job involves.

5

It's not too late to volunteer your free time for the sake of your curriculum vitae. Write off and offer your services free. Then impress your colleagues by learning fast and being nice to everyone. Who knows, they may even offer you a job. And you can still claim unemployment benefit while you're volunteering, so long as you make an effort to find paid employment.

6

It will take more than an impressive curriculum vitae and a smart suit to get you a job but you can't go wrong with a carefully worded 'Hire me' letter mailed to prospective employers. Who knows, your letter could end up on the desk of a compassionate employer. What have you got to lose?

5 Word building

There are many words and phrases in English with the word 'hand', for example *first-hand experience*. Match the words and phrases given in *italics* in A with the meanings a–h in B.

A

1 Living so close to the shops is very *handy*.
2 I'd love a new car but all I can afford is a *second-hand* one.
3 The stadium was almost empty. There were only a *handful* of people there.
4 Could you *give me a hand* with the dishes, please?
5 Emergency services were *on hand* in case there was an accident.
6 Having lived in Paris for 20 years, he must know it *like the back of his hand*.
7 I've had enough of this job. I'm *handing in* my notice today.
8 I don't know how he manages to run such a big business *single-handed*.

B

a a few
b near and ready to help if needed
c give to someone in authority
d convenient
e help
f without any help
g very well
h not new, used

Grammar

1 Relative pronouns

➤ Grammar reference, Student's Book, page 206

Fill the gaps in these sentences with appropriate relative pronouns. There may be more than one possible answer. Add commas if the clause is non-defining.

1 'The 10.05 from London Liverpool Street to Norwich _____ is due to arrive at platform 1 will call at Colchester, Ipswich and Norwich.'

2 We'll have the party next Friday _____ is the day _____ he comes out of hospital.

3 The golden eagle _____ eggs are stolen by unscrupulous collectors is now an endangered species.

4 What's the name of the girl _____ got married to Chris Small? Is it Louise?

5 Can you think of any reason _____ he might have done it?

6 I don't know of any restaurants _____ you can get a decent meal for under £15 nowadays. Do you?

7 What's the name of that singer _____ record was number 1 last month? The one _____ writes his own songs.

8 Rangers' second goal _____ was scored in the final minutes of the game won them the cup.

9 Sally's going out with someone _____ she met at Jason's party.

10 Not surprisingly, we never got back the things _____ we'd reported stolen.

11 We'll be staying at the Seaview Hotel _____ we stayed last year.

12 The best time to go to Scotland is June _____ the nights are longer and the weather is warmer.

13 I've decided I don't like the shoes _____ I bought on Saturday. I'm going to take them back.

14 The Hilton is expensive _____ is what you'd expect. After all it is a 5-star hotel.

15 The girl over there in the red dress _____ is talking to John used to go to my school.

2 Use of English

Complete the second sentence so that it has a similar meaning to the first sentence. Use up to five words including the word you are given. Do not change this word.

1 The party wasn't very interesting so we left early.
   rather
   Because _____, we left early.

2 The personnel manager, who I spoke to about the problem, said she would look into the matter.
   whom
   The personnel manager, _____ about the problem, said she would look into the matter.

3 Although the exam was quite easy, I don't think I've passed.
   quite
   It _____ but I don't think I've passed.

4 He stupidly left his car door unlocked.
   foolish
   He left his car door unlocked, _____ thing to do.

5 Jon seems to be very interested in buying Pete's old car.
   lot
   Jon is showing _____ in buying Pete's old car.

6 Jason has bought a car with a sun-roof.
   which
   The car _____ a sun-roof.

7 The robbers escaped in a stolen car.
   got
   The car that _____ was stolen.

8 Tom Cruise has appeared in many box-office hits but is especially good in this role.
   particularly
   Tom Cruise, _____ in this role, has appeared in many box-office hits.

3 Use of English

Most of the lines in this text contain an unnecessary word. A few of the lines are correct. Read the text carefully, find the extra words and mark them. Tick any lines that are correct. Two examples are given.

Being an au pair

0	I wanted to go abroad for two reasons: to prove I could	✓
00	live on my own and to give myself <u>lot</u> more time to think	
1	about what I had wanted to do with my life. In the end, I	
2	decided to go to Germany as an au pair because of my	
3	German was quite good and because it wasn't too much	
4	far away if I did got homesick. I stayed for a year. Some	
5	days it was fun but others I wished for I was at home	
6	with my mother looking after me. It was quite a boring	
7	most of the time. I had to look after a three-year-old	
8	boy and do some of housework. I also had to babysit	
9	three times a week and work all day Saturday as well as.	
10	My only day off was Sunday, which it is not the best	
11	day of the week to be free. Some au pairs' families who	
12	help pay for their classes and travel but mine didn't and	
13	I found that it impossible to live on the pocket money	
14	what I got and I had to ask my parents for help. But it	
15	wasn't all bad. I made a few new friends and my German	
16	improved a little.	

EXAM TIP

The second time you read the text through concentrate on the grammar and the meaning.

Vocabulary

1 Word building

Read the definitions and fill in the missing letters to make an appropriate adjective with a negative prefix.

Example   Someone who never puts their things
away is   UNTIDY

Someone who:
1 doesn't like being with other people is
   _ _ S _ C _ _ B _ E
2 leaves their young children alone in the house is
   _ _ R _ _ P _ _ S _ _ L _
3 finds it difficult to plan or arrange things is
   _ _ _ _ R _ _ N _ Z _ D
4 is rude and offends people is
   _ _ _ _ L _ T _
5 has little self-confidence is
   _ _ S _ C _ R E
6 gets annoyed if they have to wait is
   _ _ P _ T _ _ N _
7 isn't concerned about other people is
   _ _ C _ R _ _ G
8 can't read or write is
   _ _ L _ T _ R _ T _

2 Jumbled sentences

Unjumble the following descriptions so that they make sense. Write each correct sentence underneath.

1 mask over was thief the a his wearing face

_____

2 hair is or natural that its colour dyed your is ?

_____

3 short-sighted glasses he to so is has wear he

_____

4 wears hair she pony-tail never her back a tied in

_____

5 30 was started when father grey going only he my

_____

6 so clothes can is petite she wear that she children's

_____

7 worry more the get more you wrinkles the you

_____

8 like has red long Karen just sister hair twin her

_____

3 Use of English

Alison William, 25, is a wardrobe mistress at the Palace Theatre in Westcliff-on-Sea, Essex.

Read through this text. Then use the word in capital letters to form a word which fits in the gap. An example is given.

ME and my JOB

The Palace is a busy (0) _provincial_ theatre with usually a month gap between shows. Once I have the (1)_____ of all the actors, I can start work. It's a (2)_____ job and I get a lot of (3)_____ out of making and adapting the clothes needed for each production.

(4)_____ is essential in the weeks leading up to a new production as the actors can be very (5)_____. It's probably only due to nerves and the fact that they must feel (6)_____ in what they're wearing.

Overall, it's an (7)_____ job and, although the pay isn't brilliant, there's plenty of (8)_____. But money is less important to me than job (9)_____. It isn't essential to have (10)_____ to get a job like this but you do have to be skilled at cutting and making clothes.

0	PROVINCE	
1	MEASURE	6 COMFORT
2	CREATE	7 ENJOY
3	PLEASE	8 VARY
4	PATIENT	9 SATISFY
5	DEMAND	10 QUALIFY

4 Phrasal verbs

Answer the questions in *italics* by ticking (✓) the YES or NO box. Then write the meaning of the phrasal verb in the space provided.

YES   NO

1 We set off at three o' clock.
   Did we arrive then?   ☐   ☐
2 The men broke out of prison.
   Did they escape?   ☐   ☐
3 I took to skating the first time I tried it.
   Did I hate it?   ☐   ☐
4 Tony let me down.
   Was I disappointed?   ☐   ☐
5 Three men held up the bank.
   Were they carrying weapons?   ☐   ☐
6 Aunt Julia gave her money away.
   Did she put it in the bank?   ☐   ☐
7 The Smiths turned down our dinner invitation.
   Did they come?   ☐   ☐
8 Dave isn't looking forward to going to university.
   Is he pleased about it?   ☐   ☐

set off   _____

break out   _____

take to   _____

let down   _____

hold up   _____

give away   _____

turn down   _____

look forward to _____

Writing

Applications ➤ Student's Book, page 96

A Read the advertisement, which appeared in the magazine BBC World. How many different trips are mentioned? Would you be eligible to apply? Why?

B Fill the gaps in these opening sentences with an appropriate word beginning with the letters given.

1 I am writing with **re_____** to your **ad_____** in this month's **ed_____** of *Worldwide Travel*.

2 I am interested in **ap_____** for the **po_____** of expedition leader, which was **ad_____** in yesterday's *Daily Post*.

3 I am writing to **en_____** whether you have any **pl_____** left on your Himalayan expedition.

4 I would like to join your African project and would be **gr_____** if you could send me further **de_____**.

C You are going to write an application to join one of the adventure projects advertised. Follow this plan.

Paragraph 1
Begin the letter in an appropriate way. Say where and when you saw the advert and which trip you are interested in.

Paragraph 2 (and 3)
Give relevant information about yourself.
• How fit are you? Do you play any sports? Have you got any walking experience? You will need to have some for the Everest trek.
• What kind of person are you? What qualities do you think you will need to have?

Paragraph 3 (or 4)
Finish the letter in an appropriate way.

EXAM TIP

You don't need to include addresses but you must begin and end your letter in an appropriate way.

Opportunity for Adventure with OXVENTURE

MIXED ABILITY ADVENTURE

John Havens (who organizes the operations of OXVENTURE) is looking for people to join him in two special projects to the forests and jungles of remote west Nepal, and on a trek to Mount Everest.

John wants to open up adventure trips to all types of people, including the disabled. He is using these trips as an exercise to assess how much of an adventure holiday could be adapted for the disabled.

The two-week trips to West Nepal in March and October will include: tiger tracking, white water rafting and wildlife safaris on the back of elephants. John will analyse the activities in Nepal to see how they can be adapted for disabled people. The group size will be quite small, with a maximum of 17, including John, a doctor and two disabled people.

The Everest Trek in mid-November is a three-week trek up to Base Camp. No climbing experience is needed, you just need to be fit enough to walk for 18 days (with a day here and there, with no walking, for rest and altitude acclimitization), in the most powerfully scenic mountain range in the world. This trip is also mixed ability.

John Havens is looking for anyone, male, female, young, old, fit or flabby, disabled or able. If you are interested in taking part, please apply in writing to,

OXVENTURE, 28 Beech Road, Wheatley, Oxford OX9 1UR.

OXVENTURE

8 Points of view

Reading

1 Before you read

What sentence would you expect someone to get for committing these crimes? Choose from the three options given in the box below, using each one once only.

1 stealing a slice of pizza _____
2 theft of items worth £60,000 _____
3 kidnapping _____

• 25 years' imprisonment • five years' imprisonment
• a caution (you are warned not to break the law again)
---

2 Reading

Read texts A–E as quickly as you can to see if your answers to 1 above were right.

3 Comprehension

Read the texts again to find the following information.

Which text mentions:

a minor crime	1 _____	
an unsolved crime	2 _____	3 _____
a change in the law	4 _____	
an unpopular sentence	5 _____	

Which text mentions someone who:

may not be telling the truth	6 _____	
has never broken the law before	7 _____	
uses a weapon	8 _____	9 _____
tries to hide their identity	10 _____	
is not arrested for a long time	11 _____	

EXAM TIP

Underline key words in the questions and scan the text for the information you need.

A

Ten policemen spent a whole day filling six vans with £60,000 worth of goods which had been taken by a 79-year-old shoplifter over the past 17 years.

The elderly woman's home in Southend, Essex, was so full of stolen property that detectives could not open the door. Once inside, they found 6,900 items still in their wrappings. These included 448 pairs of shoes, 843 jumpers, 799 blouses, 1,370 scarves, 418 hats, 1,332 necklaces, 711 dresses, 23 umbrellas, and 8 fur coats.

Despite the seriousness of the crime, the woman, who has not been named, will be released with a caution. She told police she had begun stealing 17 years ago after the death of her husband and had been unable to stop. 'She got away with it for so long because no one suspected a little old lady would steal,' said a police spokesperson.

B

William, an 80-year-old beggar is a permanent fixture outside the Bank of France in Nice on the French Riviera. He stands there every day from ten until six asking passers-by for money. On Wednesday last week the bank was held up by armed robbers and over £20 million was stolen in the most daring bank-robbery ever in France.

The gang got in by kidnapping and tying up the security guards. They then held twenty bank staff hostage as they filled their sacks. Apparently not put off by the presence of video cameras, the robbers even took off their masks during the robbery, but took the incriminating video cassette with them when they left.

The French police are still looking for the robbers and the four vehicles used in the hold-up. William has been questioned by the police. He claims that he was in his usual place all that day, but saw nothing unusual.

C

When Jerry Williams, 27, grabbed a slice of pepperoni pizza from a group of children, he probably knew he was breaking the law. What he didn't know was that it could lead to life imprisonment.

Mr Williams, who later told police he threw the pizza into the sea because it contained pork, which he dislikes, has become the latest on a growing list of criminals in California who face long prison sentences for minor offences under newly-introduced laws.

Under these new laws anyone who has committed two serious crimes, for example robbery or drug possession, automatically receives a 25-year prison sentence when they commit a third, no matter how trivial the offence may be.

Mr Williams, who told the police that he took the food as a dare, has already committed two serious offences. If found guilty of theft, he could face a life sentence.

D

Police were last night searching for an eight-year-old who attempted to hold up a sweet shop with a pistol. The boy, whose face was hidden by a balaclava hat, threw a carrier bag at the shopkeeper at a corner shop in Aston-Under-Lyne and ordered her to fill it up.

'I don't know whether he wanted the bag to be filled with sweets or money,' said the owner of the shop. 'I wasn't sure whether the gun was real or not, but it didn't look like a toy.'

He ran away when the woman pressed an alarm. The boy is described as 1.1m tall, dressed in jeans and a dark coat. A police spokesperson said, 'We are taking this very seriously, as we would in any robbery involving a firearm, fake or not.'

E

Two men who took the law into their own hands have been jailed for five years for kidnap. The sentences have provoked a strong response from residents of two villages in Suffolk who describe the two as 'model citizens'.

Both men pleaded guilty to kidnapping, expecting to receive community service, and were shocked when they heard they would have to serve a jail sentence. The man they had kidnapped, John Barnes, was a known vandal and thief who was believed to have been responsible for a series of burglaries in the neighbourhood.

A spokesperson for the villagers said that everyone was shocked. 'They were only trying to help the police. They've never done anything wrong in their lives.'

4 Vocabulary

Find words or phrases in the texts which have the following meanings. The letter of the text is in brackets.

1 paper or plastic covers (A) _____

2 set free (A) _____

3 someone chosen to speak for a group of people (A) _____

4 someone who asks people for money or food (B) _____

5 dangerous and risky (B) _____

6 providing evidence of someone's involvement in a crime (B) _____

7 armed robbery (B) _____

8 take suddenly and roughly (C) _____

9 something you do because someone asks you to prove how brave you are (C) _____

10 not genuine (D) _____

11 cause a reaction (E) _____

12 someone who deliberately damages things (E)_____

Grammar

1 Use of English

➤ Grammar reference, Student's Book, page 207

Most of the lines in this text contain an unnecessary word. A few of the lines are correct. Read the text carefully, find the extra words and mark them. Tick any correct lines. Two examples are given.

```
 0  Many people have at some time in their lives stolen      ✓
00  something from a shop. In some of cases it is something
 1  valuable, but more commonly it is something small and of
 2  little value. However, it is still the theft. It is surprising
 3  too how many people think that stealing from a large
 4  store it is different from stealing from a small shop. It
 5  must be because they do think the owners of large stores
 6  have enough money yet. It is easy to steal when you don't
 7  know the person which you are stealing from. Taking a
 8  wallet is so similar. Most people wouldn't dream of
 9  actually stealing a wallet but a surprising number
10  wouldn't hesitate to pick up one that was lying down on
11  the ground and put it into their pockets. Their argument
12  is that keeping onto something which has been lost is not
13  stealing. They may not have taken it but it doesn't belong
14  to them so in effect they are some thieves though they
15  would never admit that they were breaking with the law.
```

2 Reported speech

A Write these sentences in direct speech.
1 Andy told his wife to hurry up, adding that they were going to be late.

_____

2 Sylvia asked him if he thought she should wear her red dress or her green one.

_____

3 Andy suggested she wore her black dress.

_____

4 Sylvia told him that she couldn't because it was at the dry-cleaner's.

_____

5 Andy said he didn't care what she wore but that if they were late, he might lose his job.

_____

B Report the following conversations, using the verbs in brackets. Use conjunctions to join short sentences together where possible and make any other necessary changes. An example is given.

1 Paul: Would you like to come to my party next Saturday? (*invite*)

Paul invited Delia to his party the following Saturday.

      Pete and John are coming so there'll be some people there that you know. (*add*)

_____

  Delia: Yes, I'd love to. (*say*) What time does it start? (*ask*)

_____

  Paul: About ten, but you can come when you like. (*reply*)

_____

2 Delia: I've been invited to Paul's party. (*tell*)

_____

  Angie: When is it? (*ask*)

_____

  Delia: On Saturday. (*reply*)I don't want to go but I couldn't say no. (*add*)

_____

  Angie: Why don't you phone him on Saturday and say you don't feel well? (*suggest*)

_____

3 Delia: Are you going to go to Paul's party? (*ask*)

_____

  John: I don't think so. I went last year and it was really boring (*say*). Are you? (*ask*)

_____

4 Paul's mother: Now, don't make too much noise (*warn*). I don't want any complaints from the neighbours. (*add*)

_____

  Paul: I won't (*promise*)

_____

5 Pete: Why didn't you come to Paul's party? (*ask*)

_____

  Delia: Oh, because everyone said it would be boring (*reply*).

_____

  Pete: I really enjoyed it. (*say*) It didn't finish till after 4. Angie and John were there. (*add*)

_____

C Now rewrite these sentences in reported speech. Choose the most appropriate reporting verb from the box below, using each verb once only.

1 'Don't speak with your mouth full, John!'

   John's mother _____

2 'Remember to get your father a birthday present, Laura.'

   Laura's mother _____

3 'Don't drink the water! It's not clean.'

   The man _____

4 'Let's try that new Chinese restaurant in King Street.'

   Susie _____

5 'You really must let me pay.'

   David _____

6 'Could you type this letter again please Miss Smith.'

   The managing director _____

| ask | insist | remind | suggest | tell | warn |

3 Use of English

Read the text and fill the gaps with one suitable word.

Break the habit

Smoking is a habit that is closely linked to certain times and places. If you break these links, you (0)__can__ break the habit. The best way of doing this (1)_____ to avoid the situations where you want a cigarette. If you can't avoid (2)_____, then you will just have to fight off the temptation. Sit down and think (3)_____ when and where you usually have a cigarette. For example, do you always have (4)_____ after breakfast? Once you stop smoking, these times (5)_____ places are going to be danger spots, (6)_____ work out now how you'll cope.

It will also help (7)_____ you can make new habits to break the old one of smoking, so plan a (8)_____ new activities to replace smoking. Choose things (9)_____ will distract you and occupy your hands. Some people find (10)_____ helps if they cut down (11)_____ they actually give up. But don't look on this as (12)_____ alternative to giving up, and don't do it (13)_____ more than a couple of weeks at most. The danger is that (14)_____ could go back to smoking (15)_____ many cigarettes as before.

Vocabulary

1 Use of English

Read through this text. Then use the word given in capital letters to form a word which fits in the gap. An example is given.

Why ex-smokers are less (0) _tolerant_ of smokers than non-smokers are remains one of life's (1)_____. They are much more (2)_____ towards smokers too, in particular towards those who have tried to give up but with no (3)_____.

Ex-smokers seem to think that their (4)_____ to stop smoking makes such people inferior, rather than (5)_____ a simple (6)_____ of willpower. Ex-smokers also think that people who have never even tried to stop are totally (7)_____; they don't care at all if their smoking causes (8)_____ to others. All they are interested in is their own (9)_____ and their own (10)_____.

0 TOLERANCE	6	ABSENT
1 MYSTERIOUS	7	SELF
2 AGGRESSION	8	COMFORT
3 SUCCEED	9	PLEASE
4 ABLE	10	CONVENIENT
5 REFLECT		

2 Phrasal verbs

Fill the gaps in these sentences with the correct form of *go* and an appropriate particle. You will sometimes need to use the negative form.

back   off   out   over   through   with

1 The customs officer opened the man's suitcase and _____ carefully _____ the contents, looking for anything suspicious.

2 'Now, let's _____ the main facts of the case again in case we've missed something,' the inspector said.

3 The fish was nice but the wine they served _____ it. It was far too sweet.

4 Have you got a light? My cigarette _____ again.

5 When she retires, Mary intends _____ to Brighton, where she was born.

6 Car alarms _____ always _____ for no apparent reason.

3 Use of English

Read the text below and decide which word A, B, C or D best fits each space. An example is given.

0 A more   C over
    B above   D beyond

A new Super Hero

Superman and Batman are no longer number one in the hearts of Californians. They have a new hero, a life-size doll weighing just (0) _over_ two kilos (1)_____ Safe-T-Man (safety man). Safe-T-Man's (2)_____ is to sit in the passenger seat of cars and travel around the motorways looking as (3)_____ as possible, so frightening off anyone who is thinking of (4)_____ a crime.

The idea was thought of in Los Angeles, the world capital of the motor car, where an epidemic of 'carjackings' (stealing the car with the owner inside) has (5)_____ the cost of car insurance dramatically. Last year there were over four and a half thousand, which is a(n) (6)_____ of a dozen a day, in the Los Angeles district (7)_____.

The doll, which comes equipped with sunglasses and a baseball cap, goes on (8)_____ in department stores in the US next month for $99, although for an extra $50 you can buy one with a built-in 'screamer' alarm.

The situation poses some interesting questions. Will it entitle the owner to use the motorway lane specially reserved for cars (9)_____ two or more people? This idea was introduced in an attempt to (10)_____ pollution by encouraging people to share their cars. And will Los Angeles' criminals actually be (11)_____ by this immobile passenger?

1 A labelled
    B titled
    C known
    D called

2 A work
    B job
    C business
    D career

3 A actual
    B real
    C normal
    D true

4 A making
    B doing
    C carrying
    D committing

5 A extended
    B increased
    C grown
    D risen

6 A average
    B medium
    C amount
    D measure

7 A just
    B alone
    C only
    D merely

8 A market
    B stock
    C purchase
    D sale

9 A holding
    B including
    C carrying
    D bringing

10 A reduce
    B cut out
    C improve
    D give up

11 A taken in
    B cheated
    C persuaded
    D let down

EXAM TIP

Try to eliminate three of the four alternatives. If you still can't decide on the correct answer, make a sensible guess.

Writing

The advantages and disadvantages composition

➤ Student's Book, page 116

A If you are a smoker, answer these questions yourself. If you are not, ask someone who smokes the questions and note down their answers.
Would you stop smoking if:

1 cigarettes were very expensive _____
2 smoking was prohibited in all public places _____
3 all your friends gave up smoking _____
4 smoking was made illegal _____

B Here are some sentences from a composition which answers the following question.

> Some people think that the best way to stop people smoking would be to ban the sale of tobacco. What would be the advantages and disadvantages of such a policy?

Fill the gaps in the sentences with an appropriate word or phrase from those below. Use each word or phrase once only. There are three extra ones, which you will not need to use.

also   and   because   but   despite   if
in addition   one of the advantages   so   which

1 _____, most smokers are ordinary
   people _____ would not want to be
   involved in something illegal, _____ is
   why they would stop.
2 It would be much more difficult to buy cigarettes
   _____ many people would eventually
   give up smoking simply _____ it
   would be too much trouble.
3 _____ of banning the sale of tobacco is
   that _____ cigarettes couldn't be sold
   legally, they would not be freely available.

What is the correct order of the sentences?

_____

C The three sentences in B make up the second paragraph of the composition. You are going to write the three missing paragraphs. Use these ideas to help you.

First paragraph
• Begin by making a general statement about the question. You could mention the health hazards of smoking and the fact that many people still smoke.
• Then say what the composition is about. Try not to use the exact words given in the question.
• Finally, indicate that you are going to consider the advantages and disadvantages of this method.

_____
_____
_____
_____
_____
_____

Third paragraph
• Think of some disadvantages e.g. *It will encourage a black market economy/ Banning something often makes it more attractive.* Choose two or three of your strongest ideas and back them up with supporting statements.
• Use an appropriate phrase to introduce the paragraph and appropriate words to link your ideas.

_____
_____
_____
_____
_____
_____

Final paragraph
• Summarize your arguments. You may give an opinion but you must use impersonal language.
• You may conclude with some alternative methods which you think might be more effective.

_____
_____
_____
_____
_____
_____

This section gives you extra practice in the grammar and vocabulary covered in Units 5–8. Before you begin, remind yourself of this language by looking at the Student's Book units and the reference sections.

➤ Grammar reference, pages 204–208
➤ Vocabulary reference, pages 216–217

Grammar

1 Verb tenses

Fill the gaps with the correct past form of the verbs in brackets and including any other words given.

1 The restaurant _____ (already/close) by the time we _____ (arrive).

2 'I _____ (try) to get hold of you for ages! Where have you been?'

3 Five minutes after we _____ (arrive) at the beach it _____ (start) to rain.

4 Justin _____ (live) in a small apartment until he _____ (get) married.

5 That has to be the worst film I _____ (ever/see).

6 While Alan _____ (drive) home late last night he _____ (run out) of petrol.

7 I _____ (not/invite) Richard yet.

8 They _____ (have) dinner in an Italian restaurant before going to the cinema.

9 Before I _____ (go) to live in Spain, I _____ (think) it was a hot country.

10 'Sorry. What did you say? I _____ (listen) to Carol.'

2 Correct forms

Choose the correct form from the two choices given.
1 If we *hurry / hurried* up, we'll be on time.
2 Emily is the *eldest / oldest* in the class.
3 The teacher *told / said* John to stop *to talk / talking* while he was speaking.
4 Jane *is / has been* going out with Jim since April.

5 If you *wore / had worn* an apron, you wouldn't have got your clothes dirty.
6 *Sleeping / Having slept* badly the night before, he was exhausted.
7 Aunt Mary's present, *which / that* she'd sent him for his birthday, was a big disappointment.
8 What have you *done / been doing* with my tennis racket? I can't find it anywhere!
9 Bob suggested *should go / going* for a walk.
10 It was *quite a / a quite* good holiday despite the weather.

3 Key word transformations

Complete the second sentence using the word given.

1 The rescuers continued their search for the lost climbers. **went**
The rescuers _____ for the lost climbers.

2 Interrupt me only if it's important. **disturb**
Don't _____ it's important.

3 Monique dances so well that she's sure to win the prize. **such**
Monique _____ that she's sure to win the prize.

4 It was already too late when I discovered the truth. **out**
I didn't _____ it was too late.

5 'Have you had enough to eat, Marie?' Diane asked. **if**
Diane wanted to _____ enough to eat.

6 The disco was less crowded on Saturday. **people**
There _____ at the disco on Saturday.

7 I tend not to answer her letters immediately. **usually**
I _____ her letters immediately.

8 Having turned out the light, John got into bed. **switched**
John got into bed _____ the light.

9 'Don't speak with your mouth full, Joe!' his mother ordered. **told**
Joe's mother _____ with his mouth full.

10 Stevenson's house, where he spent his childhood, is now a museum. **grew**

Stevenson's house, in _____, is now a museum.

Vocabulary

1 Phrasal verbs

Fill the gaps in the following sentences with one of these particles. Some particles are used more than once.

after   away   back   down   off   over   to   up   with

1 It's time Edward got married and settled _____. He must be well over thirty.

2 Could you put me _____ for a few days until I find a place of my own?

3 He's very easy-going. He takes _____ his father in that respect.

4 The bomb went _____ but no one was hurt.

5 You haven't thrown _____ yesterday's paper, have you? I haven't read it yet!

6 I didn't take _____ skiing immediately but I began to enjoy it once I'd had a few lessons.

7 I can't put _____ _____ your bad temper any longer. I'm leaving!

8 Sorry I'm late. When the alarm clock rang I must have turned _____ and gone _____ to sleep.

9 Don't let me _____, will you? I'm relying on your support.

10 I suppose I'd better start that composition. I can't put _____ doing it any longer.

2 Word building

A Work out the adjectives related to the following verbs and put them in the negative form, e.g. *unexpected*.

1 decide   _____
2 care   _____
3 create   _____
4 organize   _____
5 socialize   _____
6 experience _____
7 rely   _____
8 legalize   _____
9 educate   _____
10 believe   _____

B Now fill in the gaps in these sentences with one of the negative forms in 2A. Use each one once only.

1 It is _____ to bring drugs into the country.

2 I made a lot of _____ mistakes in the exam.

3 The referee was relatively _____. It was only the fifth match he'd refereed.

4 John is very _____. He never knows what he's supposed to be doing or when he's supposed to do it.

5 Old cars are much more _____ than new ones.

6 Sue can never make up her mind. She's so _____.

7 It's not only _____ people who make grammatical mistakes; university graduates make them too.

8 Winning the lottery was _____ luck.

9 Frances would rather stay at home than go to a party. She's very _____.

10 _____ people like me are hopeless at anything that requires imagination.

You are now ready to do Progress test 2.

9 Interaction

Reading

1 Before you read

Make a list of five places which people can visit in the area near where you live. Put these five places into the order in which you would recommend them to people visiting your area for the first time. Write 1–5 in the spaces.

_____ _____

_____ _____

_____ _____

_____ _____

_____ _____

2 Reading

Skim the text as quickly as you can and decide which two of the eight places described you would visit, if you had a day to spend in this area of Britain.

3 Comprehension

Now read the text more carefully and answer the questions below. Some questions have more than one answer. An example is given.

- Where can you see old methods of transport? **0** *B*

- Where are historical clothes used to show what life was like in the past? **1**

- Where can visitors see animals or birds from other countries? **2** **3**

- Which places provide somewhere for children to play? **4** **5**

- Which two attractions are situated in the same village? **6** **7**

- Where could you see exhibits related to farming? **8**

- Where would you go for sports or exercise? **9**

If you're on holiday in Britain, why not come to the Cotswolds? It's a delightful area of rolling farmland and pretty stone-built villages. If you need to forget the world for a few days, this is the place for you. These are some of the places you can visit while you're here.

A

Cotswold Wildlife Park

Situated in gardens and woodland around an old English country house, a large and varied collection of animals from all over the world can be seen in spacious enclosures. There is also a reptile house, aquarium, tropical house, a picnicking area, an adventure playground, bar, restaurant, and gift shops. Special events are organised during the summer months.

B **Cotswold Motor Museum and Toy Collection**

This is more than a motor museum, for along with the amazing cars and motorcycles there are 7000 items from the vintage motoring years. The museum is housed in an 18th century watermill on the River Windrush at the heart of Bourton-on-the-Water, one of the most beautiful Cotswold villages. In a 1920s atmosphere, you can see shops of the period, a display of old caravans, and the childhood toy collection.

- Which three places provide places for visitors to eat food they have brought themselves? **10** **11** **12**

- Which attractions are situated in buildings which once had specific uses? **13** **14** **15**

EXAM TIP

Don't read every word of the text. It isn't necessary and there isn't enough time.

C Cotswold Countryside collection

Cotswold country life is displayed here, with agricultural exhibits and a 'seasons of the year' sequence, plus Cotswold social life and an exhibition of laundry, dairy and kitchen items. Audio and video sequences and weekend events programmes. Free car parking and a range of refreshments.

D Keith Harding's World of Mechanical Music

"A unique experience in sound". An award-winning museum of antique clocks, musical boxes, and mechanical musical instruments in an old wool merchant's house in Northleach. Here also are Europe's leading restorers of clocks and musical boxes, as well as an enchanting shop with musical gifts that will bring joy to all ages.

E Perfumery Exhibition

The Perfumery Exhibition, believed to be the only one in Europe, is set in the delightful Cotswold village of Bourton-on-the-Water. This permanent exhibition includes an explanation of perfume extraction processes, an audio visual show in a specially constructed "Smelly Vision" theatre and a perfume garden where the plants have been selected for their fragrance.

F Pittville Pump Room Museum

Housed in the magnificent Pump Room overlooking its own beautiful lake and gardens, the Museum imaginatively uses original costumes to bring to life the history of Cheltenham from Regency times to the Swinging Sixties. Jewellery showing changing taste and fashion from Regency to Art Nouveau, and a spectacular collection of tiaras are also included. Special exhibitions are held throughout the season.

G Cotswold Water Park

The Cotswold Water Park, which offers an exciting variety of activities, is based on a network of lakes formed from old quarries. In addition to the water activities, which include fishing, windsurfing, sailing, and water-skiing, there are walks and picnic sites. This nationally recognised conservation area has a number of nature reserves providing opportunities to study an enormous variety of plants and local wildlife.

H Birdland Park

At Birdland you will find a huge variety of birds from all over the globe, with many wandering freely amongst the visitors. Watch our large colony of penguins feeding, swimming and playing. Relax in our newly-created picnic area, whilst keeping an eye on the children in the play area, or come to our newly-opened cafeteria. Sit in the gardens and feel the peace and tranquillity of Birdland.

4 Vocabulary

A Make a list of all the adjectives which are used in the texts to make the places sound attractive. An example is given.

delightful
_____
_____
_____

B Make lists of what would you expect to find in these places, which were mentioned in the texts. An example is given.

1 a reptile house
   snake
_____

2 an aquarium
   crab
_____

3 a children's play area
   swing
_____

4 a kitchen
   oven
_____

Grammar

1 Suggestions, advice and warnings

➤ Grammar reference, Student's Book, page 208

Change the suggestions and warnings (1–5) into expressions of advice, and the expressions of advice (6–8) into suggestions or warnings. In each case, use up to five words including the word you are given.

Example
Why don't you take a couple of weeks holiday? **should**
(suggestion)
I think _you should take_ a couple of weeks holiday.
(advice)

1 You could call and see your sister while you're in London. **ought**
   While you're in London, _____ and see your sister.
2 How about writing to tell her you're coming? **were**
   If I _____ write and tell her you're coming.
3 I suggest you arrange to meet her outside the National Theatre. **should**
   You _____ meet her outside the National Theatre.
4 Why don't you phone her the day before to make the final arrangements? **ought**
   You _____ the day before to make the final arrangements.
5 And don't forget it's her birthday next Saturday, or she'll be really offended. **better**
   You _____ forget it's her birthday next Saturday, or she'll be really offended.
6 You shouldn't drink so much coffee late at night. **less**
   I suggest _____ late at night.
7 And you should eat more fruit and vegetables. **why**
   And _____ more fruit and vegetables?
8 You'd better not eat any more chocolate – you'll become addicted. **otherwise**
   Stop _____ become addicted.

2 Ought to / should / could

Fill the gaps in these sentences with *ought to* (or *should*), or *could*.

1 You really _____ phone to say you're going to be late.
2 By the time I was eight I _____ beat my father at tennis.
3 If everything goes according to plan, the plane _____ land at 7.45 local time.
4 _____ I use your phone, please? It's an emergency.
5 You _____ watch that TV programme – it's really exciting.
6 It's suddenly gone very dark. It _____ start raining at any moment.
7 I'll try phoning John again – he _____ be home by now.
8 If he's not in, you _____ always leave a message on his answer phone.

3 Contrasting link words

Fill the gaps in this story with one of the contrasting words or phrases below. Use each one once only. In some cases, more than one answer is possible.

| but | despite | however | in spite of |
| even though | | although | |

What a day! We decided to catch the early train
(1)_____ we knew it would be full of people going to work. We got to the station with plenty of time to spare, only to find out that the train was running 20 minutes late. We decided to have coffee while we were waiting (2)_____ the machine was broken and the restaurant was still closed.
(3)_____ feeling cold and a little annoyed, we weren't going to let this bad start spoil our day.
(4)_____, when it was announced, ten minutes later that the train had actually broken down, we nearly gave up and went home.
(5)_____, of course, we were very disappointed, we were determined to enjoy the day. We eventually arrived in London two hours later than we'd planned. In the end, (6)_____ everything, the day went very well.

4 Use of English

A According to Julia Newman, which of these factors explain her son's behaviour? Read this text quickly to find out.
1 the kind of TV programmes he watches
2 he likes violent video games
3 the fact that he's 14 years old
4 he has an unusual interest in violence

B Now read the text more carefully, filling each gap with one suitable word. An example is given.

The *trouble* with Andy

Worried mother, Julia Newman says that her 14-year-old son, Andy, is bad-tempered and constantly arguing (0) _with_ the rest of the family and she's under no illusions about the cause of the boy's personality change.

'It's his age – his body's changing, he's (1)_____ pressure at school and he's started thinking (2)_____ a career,' explains 36-year-old Julia.

'But (3)_____ thing I'm sure about, Andy's behaviour (4)_____ nothing to do with what he watches on TV or the video games he plays. It's normal (5)_____ a boy of his age to be difficult and to have an interest in violence. 'I hardly (6)_____ stop Andy from watching anything on TV – it (7)_____ be impossible to anyway, at his age. We've discussed violence and he knows the difference between right and wrong. (8)_____ something is coming up on TV or on video that I feel will upset him, I explain (9)_____ him why I think it's unsuitable.

'(10)_____ ban him from watching anything would simply make it (11)_____ attractive. And anyway, some of his computer games are just (12)_____ violent. In some of them people get shot or stabbed. I've asked Andy (13)_____ games like this are more popular than the others. He says it's the graphics and the complexity of the game (14)_____ make it good or bad rather (15)_____ the violence. A few children I know do dreadful things, but it can't just be because they've seen violence on the screen.'

Vocabulary

1 Word families

This table contains words from the texts in this unit of the Workbook. Fill the gaps with the missing words. The first one has been completed as an example.

	noun	verb	adjective	adverb
1	variety	_vary_	varied	X
2	_____	X	spacious	X
3	addition	_____	_____	_____
4	complexity	X	_____	X
5	violence	X	_____	_____
6	_____	_____	_____	imaginatively
7	_____	include	_____	_____
8	_____	select	_____	_____
9	explanation	_____	_____	X
10	_____	recognize	_____	_____

2 Wordsearch

➤ Vocabulary reference, Student's Book, page 217

Find the sixteen 'travel' words in this wordsearch. There are nine types of transport and seven places connected with travel. Words can run forwards or backwards, up or down, or diagonally.

```
A A I R T A O B M C
F I N T R A I N O M
P B R R O A D S T O
E C I P S E A T O T
R O C K O L M A R O
A A A A E R O T B R
I C R O O F T I I W
L H D I X A T O K A
F E R R Y W I N E Y
O P A L P L A N E T
```

3 Use of English

Read this text advertising holidays in Finland. Then use the word given in capital letters to form a word which fits in the gap. An example is given.

RELAX IN FINLAND

If you want a more (0)_enjoyable_ holiday that's better value, forget about (1)_____ beaches and traffic jams and come to Finland.

Finland is the world in its (2)_____ state: fresh, bright and completely (3)_____. You'll find the brilliant sunshine, pure air, clear (4)_____ streams and our blue lakes – all waiting to welcome you.

Today Finland is less (5)_____ than ever before. In (6)_____ with many other holiday destinations we offer (7)_____ good value for money. Our hotels and restaurants are as (8)_____, efficient and (9)_____ as ever.

Whether you want a short break, a week's lakeside (10)_____, or a fortnight of golf, sailing and fishing, Finland offers (11)_____ experiences at unbeatable prices.

(0)	ENJOY	(6)	COMPARE
(1)	CROWD	(7)	EXCEPTION
(2)	NATURE	(8)	COMFORT
(3)	SPOIL	(9)	FRIEND
(4)	POLLUTE	(10)	RELAX
(5)	EXPENSE	(11)	FORGET

4 Phrasal verbs

A Write the phrasal verbs which mean the same as definitions 1–8, by matching a verb and a particle from the lists below.

1 start doing something   _____
2 raise (a child or a subject of conversation)   _____
3 postpone   _____
4 begin to like   _____
5 introduce (a rule or a law)   _____
6 publish   _____
7 extinguish a fire   _____
8 accommodate   _____

VERBS   bring   take   put
PARTICLES   up   out   off   to   in

B Fill the gaps in these sentences with the correct form of five of the phrasal verbs in A above.

1 Rolls Royce have just _____ a new model.
2 It took them nearly six hours to _____ the fire.
3 I know you hate going to the dentist, but you can't keep _____ it _____.
4 You can't go home now – it's too late, but we can _____ you _____ for the night if you like.
5 Can't we just stop talking about it now. I don't know why you _____ the matter _____ in the first place.

Writing

Transactional letters

➤ Student's Book, page 127

A As you read this letter for the first time, choose appropriate expressions from this list to fill the gaps.

at the head of this letter
for whatever reason
to recover the cost
for a period of six months
to discuss the situation
within five days

VIDEO INTERNATIONAL CLUB
Queen Mary Avenue,
Edgehill BG1 2PR

March 30 1996

Dear Club Member,

We are writing to inform you that the following video cassettes borrowed by you on March 22 are now seven days overdue.

Title(s)
Raiders of the Lost Ark
Aladdin
Terminator

According to our rules, all videos must be returned
(1)_____ of being taken out.
Customers who do not observe this regulation may
have their club membership withdrawn (2)_____
_____.

If, (3)_____, you are unable to
return the above videos, please phone or write to our
Branch Manager, (4)_____.

If the videos are not returned and we have not heard
from you within four days from the date (5)_____
_____, we shall assume that you no longer
wish to remain a member of our club, and we shall
start legal proceedings (6)_____
of the missing videos.

We look forward to hearing from you.

Yours faithfully,

B How would you feel if you received the letter from your local video rental shop?

C You wish to continue to be a member of Video Club International, so you are going to write a letter to the Branch Manager. Here is a suggested paragraph plan for your reply.

Paragraph 1   Apologize to the Video Club for the trouble you have caused.

_____

_____

_____

Paragraph 2   Give a convincing explanation as to why you have not been able to return the videos.

_____

_____

_____

Paragraph 3   Say what you intend to do now about the videos.

_____

_____

_____

Paragraph 4   Promise that this situation will not arise again.

_____

_____

_____

Write 120–180 words in all, in an appropriate style. Finally, check your grammar, spelling and punctuation.

EXAM TIP

Try to think yourself into the position of the writer and then write from this point of view.

Restrictions

Reading

1 Before you read

The following article is about UFOs (Unidentified Flying Objects), or 'flying saucers' as they are more commonly known. Tick any of the words below that you think will be included in the text.

alien _____	asleep _____	believe _____
disappear _____	exist _____	escape _____
fly _____	light _____	memory _____
moon _____	sky _____	space _____
star _____		

2 Reading

As you read the article, check your answers to 1 above and think about what information could be in the missing paragraphs.

3 Comprehension

Now read the missing paragraphs A – F and try to fit them into the correct gaps in the article. There is an extra paragraph which you do not need to use.

A The couple stopped to observe the UFO through binoculars and thought they could see people aboard. To escape from what they were sure was an alien spaceship, they took the back roads and arrived home 2 hours late.

B Five days later, the missing woodcutter returned home with an equally amazing story. He said he had woken up on the UFO and found himself surrounded by creatures with no hair and with half-formed faces.

C At the time his story received national publicity, some people calling it the most impressive case of its kind. However, Ground Saucer Watch, an organisation that investigates UFO cases, concluded that the story was a hoax.

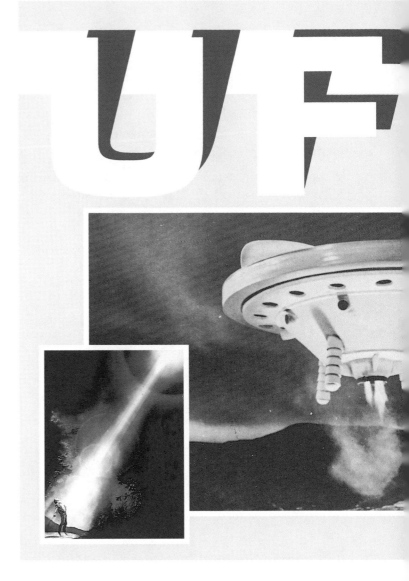

D The young man, Frank Fontaine, disappeared for a week during December 1979, apparently kidnapped by a UFO. He then reappeared in exactly the same spot as two friends watched. Fontaine said he remembered nothing of the experience.

E Fourteen years later, in 1975, one of the most famous 'kidnappings' of all took place in the USA. This extraordinary event happened in a small town in Arizona, when a team of woodcutters who were working in a remote forest area returned home with a strange story of how one of their group had disappeared in the forest.

F The first recorded case of this kind was in the 1950s when George Adamski claimed that he had been given rides in flying saucers belonging to people from Venus, Mars and Saturn. He said that two beautiful young women took him to cities on the far side of the moon.

sightings

Visitors from space are the subject of 20th century fairy tales, yet millions of normal people believe that they are real. Some people maintain that they have been visited or even kidnapped by aliens. But is there any real proof?

| 1 |

Another early case of alien kidnapping took place a few years later in 1961, when an American couple, Betty and Barney Hill, were chased by a UFO while driving home one night in New Hampshire.

| 2 |

A week later Mrs Hill began to dream that they had not escaped, but had been taken on board the spaceship and medically examined. Under hypnosis, she told a psychiatrist a detailed story of events on the spaceship, including seeing a star map, marked with the aliens' trade routes.

| 3 |

They had, apparently, seen their friend Travis Walton knocked unconscious by a blue-green light from a flying saucer. They found this so terrifying that they did not stay to see what happened next but drove off as fast as they could.

| 4 |

These 'people' then put a mask over his face and he fell asleep again, remembering nothing else until he awoke in the forest near to where he had disappeared.

| 5 |

Now, over thirty years later and despite the fact that there is absolutely no hard evidence that the earth has ever received visitors from space, the results of several American surveys indicate that the majority of people are convinced that UFOs exist.

EXAM TIP

Don't forget to look for any language connections between the paragraphs, such as reference words, linkers and sequencing words.

---

4 Vocabulary

A What are the nouns related to these adjectives from the article?

1 real _____

2 terrifying _____

3 amazing _____

4 national _____

5 famous _____

6 beautiful _____

B What are the nouns related to these verbs from the article?

1 disappear _____

2 indicate _____

3 convince _____

4 observe _____

5 conclude _____

6 publish _____

Grammar

1 Modal verbs

➤ Grammar reference, Student's Book, page 209

A Fill the gaps in these sentences with the appropriate forms of the modal verbs below. In some cases, more than one answer is possible.

should   must   need to   have to

1 _____ make so much noise? I'm trying to get to sleep.

2 You really _____ ____ come and see us next time you're here. We haven't seen you for ages.

3 Here's my work telephone number in case you _____ get in touch with me in a hurry.

4 The policeman said 'You _____ carry your passport at all times. It's the law.'

5 On Sunday I woke up with a bad toothache. I _____ make an emergency appointment to see the dentist on Monday.

6 You _____ take more care of yourself. You're looking very tired.

7 You know I'd love to come out tonight, but it's impossible. I _____ finish writing this report by tomorrow morning.

8 If I'm going to help you, I really _____ know more about your situation.

B Fill the gaps in these sentences with one of the negative modal verb forms below and the correct form of the verb in *italics* in brackets. In some cases, more than one answer is possible.

mustn't   didn't need to   don't need to   don't have to
needn't   didn't have to   needn't have

1 In many countries school children _____ (wear) a uniform.

2 You _____ (drive) after you have drunk alcohol. It's against the law.

3 You _____ (give) me a lift. I can easily catch a bus.

4 The last time I crossed the French–German border I _____ (show) my passport.

5 You _____ (bring) your umbrella after all. It hasn't rained once since we got here.

6 I _____ (forget) to go to the bank. I've got no cash left.

7 The arrangements have all been made. There's nothing left to do, so you _____ (worry) about a thing.

8 We won two tickets for the concert, which meant we _____ (pay) anything.

2 Use of English

Complete the second sentence so that it has a similar meaning to the first sentence. Use up to five words including the word you are given. Do not change this word.

1 In Britain you can't ride a bicycle on a motorway. **allowed**
In Britain you _____ a bicycle on a motorway.

2 We left home too late to catch the 9 o'clock train. **enough**
We didn't _____ to catch the 9 o'clock train.

3 You can't smoke in most cinemas these days. **permitted**
These days, _____ in most cinemas.

4 John will never be picked for the team if he doesn't spend more time training. **unless**
John will never be picked for the team _____ more time training.

5 After the fight John was not allowed into the club for a month. **banned**
After the fight John _____ the club for a month.

6 'I'm afraid you're not old enough to open a bank account.' **too**
'I'm afraid you're _____ open a bank account.'

7 It's a public holiday tomorrow, so it's not necessary for me to go to work. **need**
It's a public holiday tomorrow, so _____ go to work.

8 I was never allowed to stay the night at a friend's house. **let**
My parents never _____ the night at a friend's house.

9 I wouldn't want my car to go any faster. **enough**
My car _____ me.

10 That was a very difficult book – I couldn't
understand it. **too**
That book was _____ me to
understand.

3 Use of English

Most of the lines in this text contain an unnecessary
word. A few of the lines are correct. Read the text
carefully, find the extra words and mark them. Tick
any lines that are correct. Two examples are given.

0   My mother is always saying <u>me</u> I think too

00 much about myself, though, in my opinion   ✓

1   I don't be think about myself nearly as much

2   as she does. She's always telling to me not to

3   be so much fashion-conscious. She says I'm

4   too fussy about my appearance. But most of

5   people at school think I'm scruffy and untidy.

6   I am think she is jealous, but actually she's

7   quite a pretty herself and I must admit she

8   often buys me the nice clothes. How can I

9   make her to see that all my school friends

10 will wear make-up and spend a lot of time

11 looking at themselves in the mirror. She

12 thinks I'm unusual. My brothers make a fun of

13 me as well as, and that's quite upsetting

14 because I feel they should at least take the

15 trouble to understand me why I am like this.

EXAM TIP

Make sure you haven't marked more than one word
in a line. (In the exam, transfer only one word to the
answer sheet.)

Vocabulary

1 Clothes

➤ Vocabulary reference, Student's Book, page 218

A Make lists of words under these headings.
1 Clothes that keep people warm and dry.
2 Clothes people wear to keep cool.
3 Clothes that are often made of leather.
4 Words for clothes that can follow the phrase
a pair of . . . .
5 Clothes usually worn by women.
6 Clothes usually worn by men.

B Sort out these jumbled words for items of clothing
and then match them with one of the definitions a–h
below.

1	TELB	_____	5	PRESSLIP	_____
2	DRAGCAIN	_____	6	JAYSPAM	_____
3	TREEB	_____	7	REWETAS	_____
4	ORANKA	_____	8	FRASC	_____

a another word for pullover or jumper
b used to stop trousers or jeans from falling down
c worn round your neck to keep out the cold
d flat round hat often worn by French people
e worn in bed at night
f soft shoes worn indoors
g weatherproof jacket with a hood
h kind of pullover which opens at the front

2 Use of English

Read the text below and decide which word, A, B, C, or D best fits each gap. An example is given.

0   A next   C close
    B near   D nearby

THE STORY OF
Dr Martens

It's 1945. In the German town of Seeshaupt, (0) *near* Munich, Dr Klaus Martens limps along the streets in (1)_____ of his friend – engineer Dr Herbert Funck. Martens, straight from the army, has had a skiing accident in the Bavarian Alps and (2)_____ his foot. To make walking easier while it (3)_____, he has made himself a pair of shoes with a (4)_____, air-cushioned sole and now he wants his friend Funck's opinion. Dr Funck is amazed by the effectiveness of his friend's (5)_____ and the two men agree to develop and produce the shoes together.

(6)_____ 1959 the new shoes – then named 'Dr Martens' – were selling (7)_____ Europe, and the two men decided to find a company to produce them in Britain. After much discussion, they picked a shoe company in the village of Wollaston in Northamptonshire. On 1st April 1960 the first boot (8)_____ off the production line.

By the late 1960s, no skinhead* was (9)_____ dressed without a pair of Dr Martens 'cherry-reds'. But thousands of pairs of the boots were also being bought for their practicality by factory workers and by people doing a range of outdoor jobs. Their (10)_____ of durability, comfort and style has seen Dr Martens footwear gain acceptance by all types of people – from bankers to policemen, and rock stars to nurses. The boots (11)_____ at the centre of every trend – through the punk rock of the 70s to the designer footwear of today and the fashions of tomorrow.

_____

* **skinhead**: young person with shaved head, or extremely short hair. Skinheads have been associated with violent behaviour.

1   A hunt
    B search
    C look
    D chase

2   A injured
    B wounded
    C harmed
    D spoiled

3   A cures
    B heals
    C treats
    D relieves

4   A alone
    B unique
    C singular
    D particular

5   A plan
    B fashion
    C pattern
    D design

6   A Before
    B Until
    C By
    D Till

7   A over
    B across
    C through
    D among

8   A came
    B fell
    C ran
    D went

9   A properly
    B rightly
    C truly
    D accurately

10   A mixing
     B connection
     C combination
     D variety

11   A stay
     B keep
     C last
     D remain

3 Phrasal verbs

Use the appropriate form of one of the phrasal verbs from the list below to fill the gaps in this conversation, which takes place in a shop.

Assistant   Can I help you?

Customer   Yes, I'm (1)_____ a grey leather jacket.

Assistant   I'm afraid we (2)_____ of grey ones. They've been very popular this year.

Customer   How about blue?

Assistant   Yes, there's this one in blue. Would you like to (3)_____ it _____?

Customer   Yes, please. I'll just (4)_____ my coat _____ first.

Assistant   Here let me help you to (5)_____ it _____. It really suits you.

Customer   Yes, it's not bad. Actually the main reason I like leather jackets is that they just never (6)_____. They last for years.

| look for | put on | sell out |
| take off | try on | wear out |

Writing

Articles

A Complete these sentences about first and final paragraphs of articles, using words from the list below. There are three more words than you need.

answer   opinion   relevant   strong   thinking
asking   personal   round off   summarize   title
difficult   problem   situation   surprise   topic
example   reader

Techniques used in first paragraphs

1 Give an interesting _____ ___, to illustrate the _____ of the article.

2 Describe an unusual scene or _____.

3 Speak directly to the _____, about something _____ to them. This may include asking _____ questions.

4 _____ or interest the reader by expressing _____ opinions.

5 Present a puzzle or a _____ which needs an _____.

Purposes of final paragraphs

6 To _____ the main point(s) of the article.

7 To leave the reader _____ or wondering.

8 To express a final personal _____ on the theme of the article.

9 To _____ the article.

B Here are the second and third paragraphs of an article about the legal rights of teenagers. As you read them, think about how you could start and finish the article. Note down brief ideas.

You can die for your country, but you can't vote

Paragraph 1

_____

_____

_____

_____

_____

_____

Paragraph 2
In Britain, a boy of 17 can be a pilot or a businessman, but he cannot be a soldier or a husband without his parents' permission. He can buy guns and cigarettes, but cannot vote in an election or drink in a pub.

Paragraph 3
Teenagers everywhere find the laws that control them frustrating, but many understand the need for restrictions. 16-year-old Beth Jordan says: 'Having guidelines helps – it makes you feel you're growing up. If you could do anything at any age, it'd be different. Actually, I think what your family or friends do matters more than laws.'

Paragraph 4

_____

_____

_____

_____

_____

_____

C Think about these questions, in preparation for writing the first and final paragraphs.
1 Who might this article have been written for? Parents, teachers, teenagers, or general readers?
2 What is your opinion on the subject of teenagers and the law? Do you agree with Beth Jordan's ideas in the third paragraph?

Using your ideas and the information in A, write the two paragraphs in not more than 80–90 words. It is probably better to make the first paragraph longer than the final one.

EXAM TIP

The opening sentence of an article should introduce the topic and make the reader want to continue.

11 Speculation

Reading

1 Before you read

A You are going to read an article about a project called Biosphere 2. Look at the pictures and decide what kind of project you think it is. Then read paragraphs A and B to see if you were right. Don't read the rest of the article yet.

B If you were the journalist who was going to interview Sally Silverstone, what questions would you ask her?

_____

_____

_____

_____

_____

_____

2 Reading

As you read the whole text for the first time put a tick next to any questions in 1B above which are answered.

3 Comprehension

Read the text again and answer these questions. If the information is found in more than one paragraph, this is indicated.

Which paragraph or paragraphs refer to:

what they did in their free time	1
the lack of variety of food	2
how Ms Silverstone feels about the project	
	3 4 5
relations between group members	6
Ms Silverstone's background	7
a failure they had	8
Ms Silverstone's morning routine	9 10
Ms Silverstone's character	11
public reaction to the project	12

The Biosphere experiment

They had parties, TV and toilets, but no way out. Sally Silverstone talks to Phil Reeves about her two years in a giant greenhouse.

A
You would probably think that Sally Silverstone was a fairly average sort of person school in London; university at Sheffield; voluntary work overseas until you found out that she had just spent two years living in a gigantic greenhouse in the Arizona desert, isolated from the outside world.

EXAM TIP

Check that you haven't left any answers blank and be careful to transfer all your answers to the answer sheet.

4 Reading between the lines

1 '_Some said that the project had more to do with selling T-shirts than science._' What are the organizers of the project being accused of in this statement?
2 Do you think Sally Silverstone was one of the 'leaders' of the group? Give reasons.

B But in person, Ms Silverstone does not seem strange. With her denim jeans, short hair and sensible sandals, she looks like an ordinary, practical field worker. She is open, friendly, humorous, and enthusiastic about her time in Biosphere 2, a giant steel and glass structure in which scientists are trying to create a closed, ecological system.

C Ms Silverstone was one of two Britons in a group of eight researchers who in September returned to the outside world. Their return was met with some criticism. Some said that the $150m (£100m) project, which attracts huge numbers of tourists, had more to do with selling T-shirts than science. But, as Ms Silverstone talked about her life in Biosphere 2, it was apparent that none of the criticism had reduced her excitement about the project.

D 'I am an early riser so I would get up just before dawn, and spend some time thinking about what had to be done during the day. Then I would milk the goats, and after that I would pick the day's fresh fruit and vegetables lettuce, tomatoes, peppers, papayas and bananas and take them to the kitchen.

E The diet was quite monotonous. We always had porridge for breakfast. This was made from grain and sweetened with bananas. And usually potatoes and beans too. We only had a very small amount of animal produce. Meat was a big treat. We might have a small piece once a week, but never for breakfast. We also had a lot of different herb teas. We used to make them from mint and orange leaves.

F After breakfast everyone worked on the agriculture. We tried to grow lots of different crops but we never knew what would succeed. The bananas grew surprisingly well despite the low light levels. So did sweet potatoes. But the white potatoes got infected with a species of beetle, which destroyed them. We couldn't use pesticides because we don't use any chemicals in the Biosphere except ones which we know are non-damaging to the system.'

G I asked about living conditions and how they had passed the time when they weren't working. I was told they lived in smart, if small, two-storey apartments, complete with computers, televisions, flushing lavatories and showers, which used recycled water. 'We were in constant contact with the outside world, mostly by telephone. In the evenings we read, watched telly or listened to music'.

H And did they get on? Ms Silverstone insisted that the group of four men and four women had got on well. 'We knew that if we spent our time and energy arguing about petty things, it would have been really hard to keep the project going. But there were one or two fights', she admitted. 'They were usually about how to run the place and what to do next'.

I Now that Sally Silverstone is back in the real world, she is training the next team the project is scheduled to last 100 years. But she hardly pauses when you ask if she plans to go back into the Biosphere one day. 'Absolutely,' she says, grinning happily. 'I can't wait!'.

5 Vocabulary

Explain in your own words what the following words and phrases from the article mean. The paragraph references are given in brackets.

1 gigantic (A) _____

2 sensible (B) _____

3 apparent (C) _____

4 an early riser (D) _____

5 a treat (E) _____

6 a species (F) _____

7 two-storey (G) _____

8 lavatories (G) _____

9 petty (H) _____

10 scheduled (I) _____

Grammar

1 Use of English

Fill each gap in this article with one suitable word. An example is given.

KANGA KILLERS

Our reporter Hugh Evans examines the growing trade in kangaroo meat.

In 1972 (0) __the__ Australian government introduced a quota system which allowed (1)_____ certain number of kangaroos (2)_____ be killed or 'culled' every year. Legislation was introduced because farmers claimed that the kangaroos were ruining (3)_____ crops. The problem is that (4)_____ two and a half million kangaroos can (5)_____ killed legally each year, a further two and a half million are killed illegally. The animals are killed for a variety of reasons. The main one, (6)_____, is that kangaroo meat is sold for human consumption – usually in the form of steaks – or (7)_____ used as pet food. There are also thousands of dollars to be made (8)_____ the sale of their skins.

The environmental group Greenpeace and Australia's Animal Liberation (AAL) are now campaigning for a ban (9)_____ the sale of all kangaroo products. They hope that (10)_____ will stop unscrupulous farmers killing the animals for profit. A spokesperson for

AAL said, ' People aren't concerned because (11)_____ are still over six million kangaroos in Australia so they are hardly (12)_____ endangered species. People just don't care about issues like this (13)_____ there is a real threat. But we know certain types (14)_____ already become extinct (15)_____ some areas. We must act now before it is too late.'

2 Possibilities and probabilities

➤ Grammar reference, Student's Book, page 211

Choose an appropriate modal verb in an appropriate tense to rephrase the parts of the sentences in *italics*. An example is given.

must   can't   could   might

Example
Wife: Was the meal all right? Heather and Dave didn't eat much.
Husband: It was very nice. *Maybe they weren't hungry.*
They might not have been hungry.

1 Sally: Well, I suppose *it is possible that I misheard the name.*

   _____

2 Janis said she'd be here by one if she managed to get away. It's quarter past now so *I'm sure she isn't coming.*

   _____

3 Susie: Is Alan coming to the party?
   Julie: *Maybe I'll invite him.* I haven't made up my mind yet.

   _____

4 Fran: Oh no! This isn't my suitcase!
   Julian: *You probably took* the wrong one by mistake. Is there a name anywhere?

   _____

5 Angie: Sharon tried out that cheese soufflé recipe you gave her when we were round on Saturday but it was a bit of a disaster. It didn't rise.
   Nicky: *The oven probably wasn't* hot enough.

   _____

6 Lynne: Which one's Val's new boyfriend?
   Liz: *It's probably* that tall guy over there with the long hair. He's the only one that looks like a musician.

   _____

3 Eight things you might regret saying!

A Read the sentences and answer these questions about each one.
- Who do you think the speaker is talking to?
- What is the situation?

Example
If you're ever in our town, look us up! (*tell*)

To a person he met on holiday. Saying goodbye at
the end of the holiday.

1 I don't mind teaching you to drive. (*offer*)

_____

2 If you're really stuck, we can hold the party at my place. (*offer*)

_____

3 What would you all like to drink? (*invite*)

_____

4 Go on, how old do you think I am? (*ask*)

_____

5 I'm pretty sure I know a short-cut. (*say*)

_____

6 How much do you want to borrow? (*offer*)

_____

7 Tell me all about it. (*tell*)

_____

B Now imagine why the person wishes he or she hadn't said these things. Write sentences with *wish* and the verb in *italics* in brackets. Here is an example.

Andrew wishes he hadn't told Pete and Phil to look him
up when they were in London. They arrived on his
doorstep last Saturday and they're still there!

_____

_____

_____

_____

_____

_____

_____

_____

_____

Vocabulary

1 Use of English

Read through this text. Then use the word in capital letters to form a word which fits in the gap. An example is given.

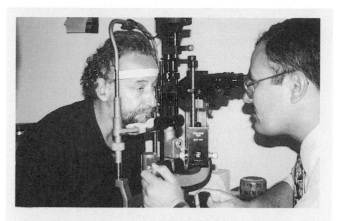

Project Orbis

Seen from the outside there is nothing (0) *extraordinary* about it. It looks like any other DC8 aircraft. The (1)_____ is inside, where all the seats have been (2)_____ by a laser (3)_____ area, a classroom and TV studio, and a fully equipped operating theatre where an (4)_____ staff of 25 surgeons and nurses carry out (5)_____ to cure the (6)_____ of as many of the estimated 49 million blind people (7)_____ as possible.

Of as much (8)_____, however, is its function of teaching (9)_____ surgeons in developing countries the (10)_____ surgical techniques.

0 ORDINARY	6	SEE
1 DIFFERENT	7	WORLD
2 PLACE	8	IMPORTANT
3 TREAT	9	EXPERIENCE
4 NATION	10	LATE
5 OPERATE		

EXAM TIP

Complete the answers you are sure about first. Make a sensible guess for any you don't know.

2 Use of English

Read the following text about pocket-size TVs and fill the gaps with the most suitable word, A, B, C, or D. An example is given.

0 A last   B continue
   C remain   D extend

Scott Newman wouldn't be without his pocket-size TV, which he mainly watches in bed. 'I only watch programmes which (0) _last_ about half an hour, as any longer (1)_____ my eyes. I use the set for general entertainment though it is also really good for (2)_____ up with current affairs. The main problem with the set is that it's not (3)_____ enough even when you use headphones. The (4)_____ is all right as long as nothing moves in front of the aerial'. Scott admits to being a gadget man, but doesn't (5)_____ buying the set since he uses it nearly every day.

Retired engineer Paul Hardcastle, has owned a pocket TV for a (6)_____ of years. 'I use it mostly in the bathroom. I wanted to use it outdoors, but the trouble is that in (7)_____ light you can't see the picture. I use rechargeable batteries as (8)_____ ones would cost too much. Paul believes that this sort of TV could be improved if the (9)_____ was slightly bigger and it didn't (10)_____ up batteries so quickly: he can only get half an hour's viewing before the batteries go flat.

1	A struggles	6	A number
	B stretches		B total
	C stresses		C sum
	D strains		D quantity
2	A coming	7	A shiny
	B keeping		B hard
	C going		C bright
	D holding		D high
3	A loud	8	A real
	B noisy		B usual
	C high		C genuine
	D strong		D ordinary
4	A response	9	A design
	B receiving		B screen
	C receipt		C face
	D reception		D display
5	A mind	10	A finish
	B disapprove		B use
	C regret		C end
	D disappoint		D take

3 Puzzle

➤ Vocabulary reference, Student's Book, page 218

Read the clues below to help you find the missing words. When you have filled them all in, you will find another word running down, which is connected with the environment.

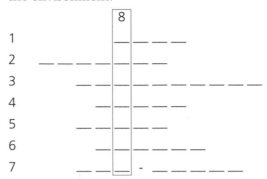

1 This kind of rain causes damage to trees and buildings.
2 Conservationists are against this type of energy.
3 This is used by farmers to make their crops grow better.
4 The sun's energy.
5 Material that is not needed and is thrown away.
6 Money is not deposited in this kind of bank.
7 An area of oil that floats on the sea.

4 Phrasal verbs

Fill the gaps in these sentences with the verb *come* in an appropriate tense together with one of the particles in the list below.

across   out   round   up   up with

1 I rarely buy hardback books – they're so expensive. I always wait till they _____ in paperback.
2 I _____ this while I was cleaning out a cupboard the other day. Is it yours?
3 You won't forget that Paula and Nick _____ for dinner on Saturday, will you?
4 I can't think what to buy Zoe for her birthday. If you _____ any good ideas, let me know.
5 When Jane _____ after the operation, she couldn't remember where she was at first.
6 I'm afraid I'll have to cancel the meeting. Something _____ at home.

Writing

The opinion composition

➤ Student's Book, page 156

A Which modern household appliances are used to do these activities nowadays?

1

2

1 _____   2 _____

B Fill the gaps in these sentences with an appropriate word or phrase from those below.

although   despite   if   in order to   so that   unless

1 People nowadays want meals which require a minimum amount of preparation _____ they can spend their time doing other things.

2 There is no point in having a lot of extra free time _____ it is used well.

3 _____ having to spend less time on housework than their mothers did, women today still work hard.

4 Nowadays, _____ something requires time and effort then people can't be bothered.

5 Women used to hang the carpets outside and beat them with carpet beaters _____ clean them.

6 _____ modern appliances mean that household chores can be done more quickly than before, they still have to be done.

C You are going to write a composition in answer to this question.

Modern household appliances have made us lazy. Do you agree?
Here are some ideas to help you decide whether you agree or disagree with the statement.

1 People do as much housework as they used to. The only difference is they do it more quickly now.

2 Women today work much harder than their mothers did.

3 Nowadays most people are not willing to spend a lot of time preparing and cooking food.

4 Most people don't spend their extra free time being active. They play computer games or watch more television.

Think of examples or explanations which back up your main points and write your ideas in note form. Here is an example for 2 above.

50 years ago
household chores = hard, physical work BUT most women no responsibilities except house / family

Today
many women full-time jobs + housework

Write 120–180 words in all. Plan your introduction like this:

• Begin by making a general statement. You could say that most people nowadays make use of modern appliances in the house, name one or two and say what they are used for.

• Then say what the composition is about, perhaps by giving a statement, e.g. Some *people think that . . . ,* saying whether you agree or disagree with it.

Remember to summarize your arguments in the conclusion and re-state your opinion, using different words.

EXAM TIP

State your opinion clearly but don't overuse personal opinion words.

Information

Reading

1 Before you read

You are going to read an article on sleepwalking. First, decide whether these statements are true or false.

1 It is possible to drive a car when you are sleepwalking.
2 On average, sleepwalkers spend over half an hour out of bed.
3 Women are more likely to sleepwalk than men.
4 If one of your parents sleepwalks, you will be likely to sleepwalk too.
5 One of the major causes of sleepwalking is overeating.

2 Reading

As you read the article for the first time check whether your answers to 1 above were right.

3 Comprehension

Choose from the sentences A–H the one which best fits each gap in the article. There is one extra sentence which you do not need to use. An example is given.

A Others include severe tiredness or the consumption of excess alcohol.
B When she woke up five hours later, she was covered in red marks.
C She did not realize that anything was wrong at first.
D She does not look forward to turning the lights out at night.
E This often leaves those specializing in sleepwalking understaffed and underfunded.
F In the majority of cases the experience is quite uneventful.
G It turned out that she had been making them in her sleep.
H It may seem amazing but all these kinds of things are possible.

Walk on the Dark Side

Mike Thomson reports on a disturbing phenomenon — sleepwalking

Dangerous as well as embarrassing, sleepwalking remains a mystery while its results can be both upsetting and unpredictable. Despite their popular image as zombie-like figures who stumble about with
5 outstretched arms, sleepwalkers are often capable of performing complex acts. Dr. Peter Fenick, a consultant neuro-psychiatrist, says their capabilities are surprising. 'I've known sleepwalkers who have got onto motorbikes, ridden horses, and driven cars.' **0** *H*

10 However, some sleep disorder experts believe that such behaviour occurs when the individual is suffering from nocturnal blackouts or amnesia. These produce what is called the 'fugue' state. In this condition the individual enters a lighter state of sleep and can cope
15 more easily with lengthier and more complicated tasks than the average sleepwalker, who is usually back in bed within 15 minutes.

Whatever the definition given, however, few people are as clear-thinking and articulate when they are
20 asleep as Janet Brierly from London, who found that her phone bill had mysteriously trebled. She later discovered why. Friends would remark on lengthy late-night calls she had made to them (many of them international), none of which she remembered.
25 **1** She has since been forced to hide her telephone in a drawer at night.

It is estimated that as many as one in three children and one in 20 adults sleepwalk at some time. Experts believe the condition is most common among children
30 and the elderly. Overall, men are more likely to sleepwalk than women, though the reason for this remains a mystery. What is now becoming clear is that sleepwalking tends to run in families. Stress or anxiety are believed to be major causes. | 2 |

35 Sleepwalking is thought to start about 90 minutes after a person goes to sleep. It occurs at the transition point between deep sleep and the more alert form of dreaming sleep. | 3 | It leads to little more than a walk round the bedroom or the opening of a few
40 drawers. Injuries most often occur when sleepwalkers believe they are somewhere they are not: windows, stairs and electrical appliances can lead to disaster.

Nancy Harrison from Wiltshire woke up shivering one night to find the bedroom window wide open and her
45 husband Robert's bed empty. | 4 | 'I assumed Robert had gone to the bathroom. But when I went to close the window, I happened to look down and there was his body lying on the lawn. I was really scared. I couldn't believe he could still be alive and I
50 dashed downstairs. But when I bent down to check if he was still breathing, I discovered he was unhurt and still asleep.'

In another instance a Birmingham woman poured hot water over herself while she was sleepwalking. She
55 was convinced that her house was filling up with ice. | 5 |

Trying to find the root cause of the problem of why people sleepwalk is not straightforward. There are several sleep laboratories and clinics around the country, but most concentrate on treating more
60 common complaints such as snoring or insomnia. | 6 |

To see a specialist you will need to be referred by your own doctor, who may first try you on sleeping pills. These work by temporarily stopping the body entering the phase of sleep which accompanies
65 sleepwalking, but their addictive nature means they are only a short-term solution.

4 Reading between the lines

1 Where do many of Janet Brierley's friends live?
2 Can you think of any possible reasons why men are more likely to sleepwalk than women?
3 When are sleepwalkers most likely to injure themselves?

5 Vocabulary

Match the following words and phrases with their meanings. The line reference number is given in brackets.

1	stumble (4)	a	become three times bigger
2	nocturnal (12)	b	most important
3	treble (21)	c	process of change from
4	overall (30)		one state to another
5	run in families (33)	d	walk in an unsteady way
6	transition (36)	e	believe; suppose
7	assume (45)	f	inability to sleep easily
8	root (56)	g	occur in members of the
9	straightforward (57)		same family
10	insomnia (60)	h	speaking generally
		i	happening at night
		j	clear and uncomplicated

6 Word building

How many of these words can you remember without looking at the article? A related word is given as a clue. An example is given.

1 danger (noun) ___dangerous___ (adjective)

2 anxious (adjective) _____(noun)

3 tired (adjective) _____(noun)

4 capable (adjective) _____(plural noun)

5 behave (verb) _____(noun)

6 consume (verb) _____(noun)

7 event (noun) _____(negative adjective)

8 injure (verb) _____(plural noun)

9 addict (noun) _____(adjective)

10 solve (verb) _____(noun)

Grammar

1 Active or passive?

➤ Grammar reference, Student's Book, page 212

Put the verb in *italics* in brackets into the correct tense of the active or passive form.

1 It's a huge company. Two thousand people _____(*employ*) there.

2 The explosion _____(*happen*) just after 9pm. Fortunately no one _____(*hurt*).

3 The hotel we stayed at was quite good. The rooms _____(*clean*) every day and the towels _____(*change*) every other day.

4 He only has himself to blame. He _____(*warn*) he could lose his licence the next time he _____(*catch*) speeding.

5 All the children _____(*send*) home when the school's central heating system _____(*break down*) last winter.

6 The watch isn't worth much but it has sentimental value. It _____(*give*) to me on my 21st birthday.

7 Five hundred employees _____(*make*) redundant since the company _____(*take over*) six months ago.

8 I wonder why Michael _____(*not invite*) to Lee's party next Saturday. Everyone else is going.

2 Use of English

Complete the second sentence so that it has a similar meaning to the first sentence. Use up to five words including the word you are given. Do not change this word.

1 More and more people are learning to play golf each year. **taken**
Golf _____ more and more people each year.

2 They say she was over 80 when she died. **said**
She _____ over 80 when she died.

3 You should throw the milk away if it smells funny. **ought**
The milk _____ if it smells funny.

4 They think Stephen's sister is living in Australia. **thought**
Stephen's sister _____ in Australia.

5 Jodie was very anxious when she lost her purse. **upset**
The loss of her purse _____ deal.

6 We expect that the new motorway will open in the autumn. **expected**
The new motorway _____ in the autumn.

7 The neighbours eventually extinguished the fire. **put**
The fire _____ _____ the neighbours.

8 The police believe the robber was wearing a dark-blue jacket and jeans. **believed**
The robber _____ wearing a dark-blue jacket and jeans.

3 Use of English

A Read the text through quickly. How many festivals are mentioned?

B Read the text again and fill each gap with one suitable word. An example is given.

From earliest times people have celebrated the end of winter and the new life that spring brings. One of the (0) _most_ important Christian festivals is Easter, (1)_____ Christians remember the death and resurrection of Jesus Christ.

Easter, (2)_____, is not the only spring festival. In Sweden, people celebrate (3)_____ end of winter (4)_____ making huge bonfires. Fire also plays an important part in the Hindu festival of Holi. In some villages children (5)_____ carried round bonfires by their mothers to protect them (6)_____ danger in the coming year. Buddhists in Thailand soak each (7)_____ in water when celebrating their New Year, (8)_____ falls in the middle of April. In Antigua in Guatemala they carpet the streets with flowers. Chinese spring parades are equally colourful, but (9)_____ of flowers they have large dragon puppets which dance in the streets.

Eggs are traditionally linked (10)_____ festivals celebrating the end of winter. As long as 3,000 years (11)_____, people in ancient China and Greece ate coloured hard-boiled eggs; 160 years ago chocolate eggs became popular in (12)_____ countries. In Britain, hot cross buns, a kind (13)_____ sweet bread, are traditionally eaten on Good Friday, the day Christ died on the cross. However, crossed buns (14)_____ been eaten (15)_____ thousands of years. People thought that marking cakes with a cross kept away evil spirits.

4 Use of English

Most of the lines in this text contain an unnecessary word. A few of the lines are correct. Read the text carefully, find the extra words and mark them. Tick any lines that are correct. Two examples are given.

0 One of the most popular dishes in Spain it is Spanish
00 omelette. Although it is not difficult to make, it requires ✓
1 a lot of preparation. The ingredients you must need are oil,
2 potatoes and onions. If you can afford it, the olive oil is
3 best. It gives the omelette a very distinctive flavour. The
4 most worst thing is peeling the onions because they make
5 you to cry. After peeling and slicing the potatoes and onions,
6 put both them in the frying pan and cook them until they
7 are soft. Meanwhile beat some eggs in a bowl and add a little
8 of salt. Add the potatoes and onions to this mixture, put it in
9 a frying pan and cook. When one side is cooked, turn it over
10 the omelette and cook the other side. Use a plate for to do
11 this. If your omelette is quite big, this is quite difficult. The
12 omelette can be eaten hot or cold. It depends that which you
13 prefer. Both are too good. Spanish omelette is nice
14 with salad and crusty bread. Try it and see if you are
15 agree with me.

EXAM TIP

There will always be a few lines which are correct. Remember to tick (✓) these lines and transfer all answers to the answer sheet.

Vocabulary

1 Use of English

Read through the following text about Bonfire Night. Then use the word in capital letters to form a word which fits in the gap. An example is given.

Fireworks on Bonfire Night

Hospitals dealt with over 750 (0)____*injuries*____ on November 5th last year. This year (1)_____ experts hope the number will be cut but this seems (2)_____ with 10 million people letting off 100 million fireworks.

Fireworks are usually safe unless they are handled (3)_____. Most accidents could be avoided if people paid more (4)_____ to the (5)_____ which are written on the box.

However, some of the most (6)_____ fireworks look the most (7)_____. The pretty coloured Roman Candle and the younger children's (8)_____, the Sparkler can cause serious burns.

Remember that no firework is (9)_____ safe. But as long as you are (10)_____, Bonfire Night will be an occasion to remember, not to forget.

0	INJURE	6	DANGER
1	SAFE	7	HARM
2	LIKE	8	FAVOUR
3	CORRECT	9	COMPLETE
4	ATTEND	10	CARE
5	INSTRUCT		

2 Phrasal verbs

A What are the missing particles that go with *get*? Use the sentences below and the number of letters indicated in the diagram to help you find the missing particles. Then match each verb with its meaning.

1 The robbers got _____ in a blue van with over a million pounds.

2 Everyone gets _____ with Dave. He's such a nice person.

3 He's been unemployed for over a year and it's beginning to get him _____.

4 It's difficult to get _____ when neither of you is earning and you've got three kids.

5 I can't get _____ passing my English exam. I really thought I'd failed it.

6 We couldn't get _____ through the front door because of the smoke and had to leave the building by the emergency exit.

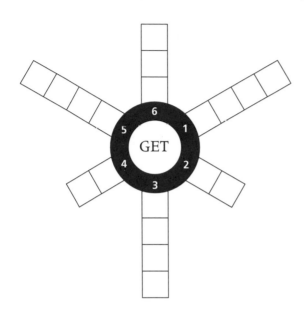

a leave or escape from a place
b manage
c recover from a shock or illness
d depress
e have good relations with someone
f escape after committing a crime

B Fill the gaps in sentences (1–8) with an appropriate phrasal verb made from one of the verbs below with the particle *up* or *out*. You will need to put the verb in an appropriate tense.

bring   carry   get   hang   run   save   take   turn

1 It must be difficult to live in the country if you _____ in a town.

2 No wonder Carole's depressed! She should _____ more instead of spending all her time at home.

3 Darren _____ all his pocket money for two months to buy his mother a birthday present.

4 I always seem _____ of time in exams. I never finish all the questions.

5 The room would look nicer if they _____ a few pictures.

6 Jeremy _____ all his money and closed the account.

7 The government plans _____ a survey into the number of people who think fox-hunting should be banned.

8 Greg _____ at Lee's party in a gorilla costume. Someone had told him it was a fancy dress party!

3 Word ladder

➤ Vocabulary reference, Student's Book, page 218

Fill in the grid by finding the answers to the clues below. The missing words are all connected with food, drink and social gatherings. The number of letters in each word is given in brackets. When you have completed the grid you should find another related word in the grey squares.

1 A bottle, a packet and a jar are all types of _____.(9)

2 The opposite of 'tough' for meat. _____(6)

3 The opposite of 'hot' for dishes like curry. _____(4)

4 To 'cook' bread, cakes and biscuits. _____(4)

5 Tiny bits of bread, cake or biscuits. _____(6)

6 Food with a salty or spicy taste; not sweet. _____(7)

7 A type of oven that uses very short electric waves to cook or heat food. _____(9)

8 An informal social meeting or party. _____(3+8)

9 If you cook something too much it is _____.(10)

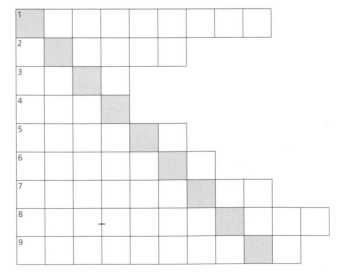

Writing

Reports ➤ Student's Book, page 169

A Read the following letter quickly and answer these questions.

1 Who is Jane writing to?
2 What is she writing about?
3 What isn't she looking forward to?

Anyway, let me tell you about the trip. It was really great but the week just flew by. We left London at 8am on Saturday June 8th but the coach didn't get to Madrid till 11pm on the Sunday night. I thought we'd never get there! Three people were sick on the coach and everyone felt too tired to do anything the first day. We were all absolutely shattered. I wish we could have gone by plane.

But everyone said it was worth it once they'd recovered. Our hotel was in the centre of Madrid, in the old part, which was really good as it meant we could walk just about everywhere. It was two-star and was fine. We only had our breakfast in the hotel. We had all our other meals out in cheap restaurants but sometimes we just had snacks in the bars. The food was really good, especially paella. The only thing I didn't like was octopus.

What did we do? Too many things to write here. Everyone agrees that the best were a visit to the Prado museum, and the excursion to Toledo. We were there when the Easter processions were on. There were men dressed up in long robes and wearing really tall, pointed hats with holes for their eyes. Amazing! We went to a bullfight as well but most people wanted to leave before the end.

The trip back wasn't as bad as the trip out as we were all so tired that we slept most of the way. The only awful thing is that I agreed to write a report for the head. It's the first time we've been on a trip abroad and he wants to know how it's gone and whether we should go again next year. Everyone that went said they'd really enjoyed it.

Write back soon,

Love Jane

B You are going to write an answer to the following exam question.

> The head teacher has asked you to write a brief report on a trip your class went on recently. She would like to know how successful it was and whether another trip should be organized next year.

You can use the information and opinions in Jane's letter. Read it again and group information and opinions in note form under these sub-headings.

Journey

_____
_____
_____
_____
_____

Accommodation

_____
_____
_____
_____
_____
_____

Visits and excursions

_____
_____
_____
_____
_____
_____

Use these notes as the basis of your report, adding an introduction and a conclusion. Write your report in 120–180 words.

EXAM TIP

Remember to state the aim and content of a report in its introduction.

Revision

This section gives you extra practice in the grammar and vocabulary covered in Units 9–12. Before you begin, remind yourself of this language by looking at the Student's Book units and the reference sections.

➤ Grammar reference, pages 208–213
➤ Vocabulary reference, pages 217–219

Grammar

1 Correct forms

Choose the correct form from the two choices given.

1 If *we'd / we* got up earlier, we wouldn't have been in such a hurry.
2 I regret *sending / to send* that letter. I wrote some very unkind things in it.
3 Some parents don't let their children *to go / go* out on weekday evenings.
4 Sarah was on the point *to go / of going* to bed when the phone rang.
5 I went to work *in spite / despite* having a high temperature.
6 Unless *you / you'll* drive more slowly, you'll have an accident.
7 There's a meeting at six o'clock, but you *don't have to / mustn't* come if you don't want to.
8 I wish my neighbours *stopped / would stop* playing such loud music late at night.
9 Why is everyone leaving the cinema? The film *mustn't / can't* have finished already.
10 My sister *sent / was sent* over a hundred cards on her eighteenth birthday.

2 Verb tenses

Fill the gaps in these sentences with the correct form of the verb in brackets.

1 What would you do if you _____(win) the lottery?
2 My sister _____(find) a ten-pound note while she _____(walk) to school yesterday.
3 The sky is very dark – I think it _____(rain).
4 By the time I _____(arrive), the football match _____(already/start).

5 I _____(just/finish) reading 'War and Peace'. It's a brilliant book.
6 If I hadn't gone to that party, I _____(never/meet) my girlfriend.
7 Good luck at the interview. I hope you _____ (get) the job.
8 After his accident last week, Jeff promised he _____(drive) more carefully.
9 When the assistant asked me if I _____(be served), I said I _____(wait) for over twenty minutes.
10 If you want to know the results of the election, I suggest you _____(listen) to the radio news.

3 Key word transformations

Complete the second sentence using the word given.

1 Maybe John's working tomorrow. **could**
John _____ tomorrow.
2 I'm really sorry Andrew isn't coming to my party at the weekend. **wish**
I really _____ to my party at the weekend.
3 Riding a bicycle on the pavement is against the law. **allowed**
You _____ a bicycle on the pavement.
4 We booked a table, but it wasn't necessary, as there weren't many people in the restaurant. **need**
We _____ a table, as there weren't many people in the restaurant.
5 In Britain you can't leave school until you're 16. **compulsory**
In Britain _____ at school until you're 16.
6 Unfortunately, Nick was too short to be a good basketball player. **enough**
Unfortunately, _____ to be a good basketball player.
7 They'll have to cancel the picnic if it rains. **be**
The picnic _____ if it rains.

8 The police are questioning two boys in connection with the accident. **are**

Two boys _____ police in connection with the accident.

9 I'm sure Alison made the announcement. I recognized her voice. **must**

It _____ made the announcement. I recognized her voice.

10 It is essential that you eat the soufflé as soon as it is cooked. **be**

The soufflé _____ as soon as it is cooked.

Vocabulary

1 Correct words

Choose the correct word from the two choices given.

1 I watched my brother as he *got on / got in* his bike and *drove / rode* away.

2 We were rather late, so we decided to *catch /take* a taxi to the station.

3 My father's just returned from a business *journey / trip* to Hong Kong.

4 Try to bear in *head / mind* what I told you.

5 We were walking in the hills when we were caught in a *heavy / strong* shower of rain.

6 You really ought to get a microwave *cooker / oven*.

7 I had a terrible headache. I just wanted to *lie / lay* down and go to sleep.

8 There have already been two price *rises / raises* this year.

9 Three armed gunmen *robbed / stole* £30,000 from a London bank late yesterday afternoon.

10 When I was two years old I fell down stairs and broke my arm. You can still see the *wound / scar* on my elbow.

2 Word building

Answer these questions with words related to the words in italics.

Example   What do you call someone who *conducts* an orchestra? *a conductor*

What do you call:

1 a person who *competes* in a race? _____

2 someone involved in *psychology*? _____

3 someone who *resides* in a particular place? _____

4 a person who *acts* on the stage or in films? _____

5 someone who *operates* machinery? _____

6 a person who *burgles* people's houses? _____

7 someone in the *civil service*? _____

8 a scientist who is a *chemistry* expert? _____

9 someone who practises *law*? _____

10 someone who works with *electricity*? _____

3 Phrasal verbs

Match the beginnings 1–10 with appropriate endings a–j. Then fill the gaps in endings a–j with the correct form of one of the phrasal verbs listed below.

1 I gave John a lift home last night.

2 Twenty people have promised to come to my party.

3 If you've got nowhere else to sleep, don't worry,

4 My mother can't wait for her holiday in Austria.

5 Please could you turn the TV down?

6 The house had been in flames for six hours

7 Do you think you could give me a lift to work tomorrow?

8 Everyone was really embarrassed.

9 I was tidying my room yesterday

10 Stuart's a very popular person.

a we can always _____ you _____ for the night.

b I'm trying to read and it _____ me _____.

c Everyone I know seems to _____ him very well.

d As it was raining hard, I _____ him _____ right outside his house.

e before the fire fighters managed to _____ it _____ .

f when I _____ some photos I'd been looking for for ages.

g Yes, of course. I _____ you _____ at seven o'clock.

h I just hope nobody _____ me _____ at the last minute.

i I don't know why he _____ the subject _____ in the first place.

j She _____ going for nearly a year now.

bring up   come across   drop off   get on with
let down   look forward to   pick up   put off
put out   put up

You are now ready to do Progress test 3.

13 Skills and abilities

Reading

1 Before you read

Try to answer all these questions.
1 When is your birthday?
2 What day of the week were you born on?
3 What day of the week did your tenth birthday fall on?
4 What day of the week was 1 April 1933?

2 Reading

Scan the text to find the answers to the following questions.
1 What is autism?
2 When was autism first named?
3 How many children are born autistic?
4 Which film is about an 'autistic savant'? (autistic savants are autistic people with particularly highly-developed skills)

3 Comprehension

Read the text again carefully and choose the best answer for each question, A, B, C or D.

1 What is particularly unusual about autistic people is that many of them have
  A extremely poor memories.
  B larger-than-average brains.
  C incredible mental abilities.
  D higher than average intelligence.

2 What does the writer mean by 'restricted' in line 39?
  A extraordinary
  B limited
  C varied
  D extensive

3 Medical research has discovered that
  A autism does not affect the sexes equally.
  B autistic people feel rejected by their families.
  C only a few autistic people suffer intense pain.
  D all autistic savants have a wide variety of skills.

Autism is a mental disease which prevents those who suffer from it from communicating with the outside world. Victims seem to live in a world of their own which, even now, doctors are unable to
5 penetrate. The illness was first given a name in 1943, and yet doctors have made very little progress in their understanding of the disease since then. According to statistics, between two and four children out of every 10,000 are born autistic.

The mysterious powe

10 Often victims are not able to speak, read or write. But what is most extraordinary about the illness is the fact that in other areas many of the children can use their brains in ways which are almost super-human. One of the more common skills these so-called autistic savants have is calendrical
15 calculation, that is the ability to say which day of the week a particular date falls on. Jackie, for instance, who is now 42, could do this from the age of six, when she first began to talk. She can tell you what day of the week it was on 1 April 1933 with scarcely a moment's hesitation. But if you ask
20 her how she does it, she'll say she doesn't know.

4 Following the success of the film *Rain Man*
  A people have given more money to research on autism.
  B the media have shown a greater interest in autism.
  C the public have become knowledgeable about autism.
  D researchers have found a cure for autism.

5 What does 'This' in line 52 refer to?
  A The Oscar.
  B The film.
  C The performance.
  D The media interest.

EXAM TIP

Don't just guess the answer. Look for real evidence in the text to support your choice.

Leslie Lemke only has to hear a piece of music once and he can play it back on the piano note-perfect. Yet he has never had any formal musical training, is blind and with an IQ of only 58 is typical of the majority of autistic savants, who
25 have well-below-average intelligence quotients. If you ask Richard the route of any bus in the London district , he will give you an answer immediately. Stephen Wiltshire has exceptional artistic talents and, like both Leslie and Richard, combines this talent with a remarkable memory, and can draw
30 buildings with complete architectural accuracy, sometimes only hours after seeing them for the first time. Other savants are able to carry out amazing mathematical computations in their heads, but cannot add up simple numbers.

of **the brain**

How savants perform such tricks is as puzzling to the
35 medical world as it is to Jackie and the others like her. Certain common characteristics have, however, emerged. Strangest of all, perhaps, is the fact that about 85 per cent of all recorded cases are male. What no one knows either is why the range of savant skills is so restricted. These include
40 music (usually the piano), calendrical or other mathematical calculation, art, extra-sensory perception, extraordinary sensitivity of touch or smell and (more unusually) mechanical ability.

It has been suggested that autistic people do not suffer; that they are perfectly happy to remain in their own world and
45 that a cure is only necessary in order to reduce the terrible pain of rejection felt by the victims' families. This controversial opinion is, however, only held by a few.

The subject became the focus of particular media interest after Dustin Hoffman won an Oscar for his brilliant
50 performance in the film *Rain Man*, where he plays the part of an autistic savant. This has increased public awareness of the disease and hopefully will result in more money being given to research and a cure being found sooner rather than later.

4 Vocabulary

A Find other words in the text which have similar meanings to the words given. Where there is more than one word with a similar meaning, this is indicated.
1 disease (line 1)
2 extraordinary (line 11), three possible answers
3 ability (line 15), two possible answers

B Match these words from the text with meanings a–e.
1 mental (line 1)
2 penetrate (line 5)
3 controversial (line 48)
4 focus (line 49)
5 awareness (line 52)

a enter and understand
b causing discussion and disagreement
c main source or object of something
d of the mind
e realization that something exists

C There are several examples of adjectives which end in -*al* in the text, for example *musical*. How many others can you find? List them.

_____

_____

D Make the following nouns into adjectives ending in -*al*.

comedy   _____

intellect   _____

culture   _____

finance   _____

education   _____

industry   _____

Grammar

1 Use of English

Read the text and fill each gap with one suitable word. An example is given.

The four-year-old undergraduate

A child prodigy of four is receiving computer lessons at Brunel University, in London. Nicholas MacMahon (0) __is__ studying at university because he is (1)_____ clever for school. A senior lecturer at the university, Valso Koshy, said (2)_____ boy was remarkably intelligent.

Nicholas spoke fluently before he was one and (3)_____ the time he was 18 months old he was taking telephone messages. This (4)_____ soon followed by conversational French. These are the trademarks of a highly-gifted child, unusual (5)_____ not unique. The strange thing (6)_____ Nicholas is his reading – he taught (7)_____ to read before he could speak. Ms Koshy, (8)_____ expert on gifted children, says Nicholas is quite exceptional. Yet 'exceptional' understates his amazing ability (9)_____ read, almost from birth. 'He was talking when he was one (10)_____ we realized from the start he (11)_____ read,' his father said. 'Soon after, he was correcting my spelling, words like *caterpillar*.

Now he identifies insects by (12)_____ Latin names'.

The list (13)_____ achievements is impressive, but frightening. A four-year-old who (14)_____ tell a Boeing 747 from a DC10, devours encyclopaedias, reads *The Daily Telegraph* and is well on the way to becoming a violin virtuoso is (15)_____ normal.

2 Use of English

Complete the second sentence so that it has a similar meaning to the first sentence. Use up to five words including the word you are given. Do not change this word.

1 Chrissie can't draw as well as her sister. **good**
   Chrissie is _____ as her sister.
2 Although she had set off late, Jenny caught the train. **managed**
   Despite setting off late, _____ the train.
3 I can't run any faster than that. **able**
   That's _____ to run.
4 Nobody thought Alan was good enough to win the championship. **capable**
   Nobody thought Alan _____ the championship.
5 I could probably touch my toes if I tried. **able**
   I _____ touch my toes if I tried.
6 'Can anyone cook trout?' she asked. **how**
   She asked if anyone _____ cook trout.
7 The accused couldn't convince the jury of his innocence. **succeed**
   The accused _____ the jury of his innocence.
8 Even if the firefighters had arrived sooner, they couldn't have saved the building. **able**
   The firefighters _____ to save the building even if they had arrived sooner.

3 Find the mistakes

➤ Grammar reference, Student's Book, page 213

Of the ten sentences in this exercise three are correct and seven contain mistakes in the question tags. Tick the correct sentences and correct those which are wrong.

Example   There are no mistakes in this sentence, ~~aren't they~~? *are there?*

1 I am on time, don't I?
2 Don't forget to feed the cat, do you?
3 We had a wonderful holiday, hadn't we, darling?
4 He hasn't got enough time, has he?
5 Nobody else was invited, was it?
6 Close the window, do you?
7 Nothing's wrong, is it?
8 I don't know your name, don't I?
9 You will remember to do it, won't you?
10 You'd rather not say, hadn't you?

4 Use of English

Most of the lines in this text contain an unnecessary word. A few of the lines are correct. Read the text carefully, find the extra words and mark them. Tick any lines that are correct. Two examples are given.

0	Having a bad memory can be dangerous. Have you ever left ✓
00	<u>from</u> the house without remembering to turn off the gas
1	and almost have caused a fire? I have. And more than once
2	time as well. Now even when I remember to do it I
3	convince to myself that I have forgotten. The picture in
4	my mind is so vivid that I rush home imagining that fire-
5	engines outside of and flames pouring through the
6	window. But of course I find everything in order.
7	Forgetting things can be too embarrassing as well. It may
8	seem like incredible but on one occasion I actually forgot
9	the name of my flat-mate. We had known us each other for
10	two years. I didn't dare ask her that – she would have
11	thought I was mad – and two whole days had passed
12	before I finally remembered. If I'm honest, I have to admit
13	that it was embarrassing both and worrying. However,
14	there are advantages. You can avoid unpleasant
15	experiences like the trips to the dentist simply by
16	forgetting you had an appointment.

Vocabulary

1 Use of English

Use the word given in capital letters to form a word that fits in the space. An example is given.

The cinema is one of the most popular forms of (0) <u>entertainment</u> in the world. Its (1)_____ means that blockbuster movies are seen by millions worldwide.

Because of this, the messages they give out are seen as (2)_____ important. Psychologists argue that film-watching isn't always (3)_____ fun and are concerned about the (4)_____ effects it may have.

Black actors and women are (5)_____ with the number and type of roles available to them. With one or two (6)_____ the latter have (7)_____ had to play simple characters dependent on strong male leading actors.

Another important concern is (8)_____ in films. With the (9)_____ in the video industry, violent films are coming into the home and are (10)_____ available to young viewers.

0	ENTERTAIN	6	EXCEPT
1	POPULAR	7	TRADITION
2	EXTREME	8	VIOLENT
3	HARM	9	GROW
4	DAMAGE	10	EASY
5	SATISFY		

2 Phrasal verbs

In this text the verb particles are missing and the letters of some words are jumbled up. Put the letters in the correct order to make a word connected with money and add the missing particles to the verbs. Use each particle once only.

up   back   down   out   off

When I decided to trade in my seven-year-old car for a new model I didn't realize what a financial trap I was getting myself into. I agreed to put (1)_____ a (2) *pioedts* of £1,500 and to pay (3)_____ the rest of the (4) *betd* in monthly (5) *misnallents*, but in order to do this I had to take (6)_____ a bank (7) *anol* at 14.5% (8) *rinteest*. Although I had been saving (9)_____ for months, I had only managed to get together £200. I worked out that I would have to pay the bank and car company a fifth of my (10) *yrasal* for the next five years and that by the time I'd paid (11)_____ all I (12) *edow*, my new car would need replacing and I'd have to start all over again.

3 Wordsearch

➤ Vocabulary reference, Student's Book, page 219

Use the clues below to help you find 14 'money' words. Words can run vertically, horizontally, diagonally and backwards, and may overlap. The number of letters in each word is given in brackets after the clue.

P	R	O	S	P	E	R	O	U	S	I
E	Y	A	P	W	E	T	I	P	C	C
N	O	M	E	A	N	O	X	S	R	A
S	T	I	N	G	Y	O	E	S	E	W
I	P	V	D	E	B	T	V	A	D	B
O	W	I	T	H	D	R	A	W	I	L
N	E	T	T	P	U	R	S	E	T	O

1 money the government pays retired people (7)
2 take money out of a bank account (8)
3 opposite of *spend* (4)
4 a salary or wage after tax has been paid: a ___ (3) salary

5 rich and successful (10)
6 money owed (4)
7 give someone money for something (3)
8 money paid for a period of work (4)
9 a small plastic card which allows you to pay for things without using money: a ___ (6) card
10 an increase in salary (4)
11 opposite of *generous* (4)
12 extra money given to e.g. a taxi driver (3)
13 small bag for keeping money, especially coins, in (5)
14 unlikely to give or spend money (6)

4 Verbs of seeing

Complete the sentences with one of these verbs in a suitable tense.

catch a glimpse   glance   look   notice
observe   scan   see   stare

1 '_____ the text quickly to find the information you are looking for,' the teacher instructed.
2 Diane says she's only had time to _____ at the report so far.
3 She looked so like her mother that I couldn't stop _____ at her.
4 On a clear day you can _____ the distant hills.
5 We _____ of the cathedral as we drove past.
6 I'm afraid I didn't see anything. I _____ the other way at the time.
7 'Michael is rather a strange person, isn't he?' Carol _____.
8 I really like Darren but he's far too good-looking to _____ me.

5 Opposites

What are the opposites of these words? The first letter and the number of letters in each word is given.

1 mean   g _ _ _ _ _ _ _
2 pay into   w _ _ _ _ _ _ _
3 lend   b _ _ _ _ _
4 valuable   w _ _ _ _ _ _ _ _
5 poor   w _ _ _ _ _ _

Writing

Applications ➤ Student's Book, page 182

A Read the advertisement and decide who can apply for a scholarship. Then read the letter. Does this applicant meet the necessary requirements?

The British Trust is offering 10 scholarships of £6,000 to foreign students who wish to do a Master's degree or one-year post-graduate diploma at a British university in one of the following subjects:

English Literature; History;
Medicine; Science; Economics.

Applications should be made in writing to George Hill, The British Trust, 10, Richmond Gardens, Birmingham B10 1AG.

B Read the letter again and choose the option A, B, C or D which best fits each gap.

1 A connection
   B reference
   C relation
   D concern
2 A demand
   B request
   C inquire
   D apply
3 A career
   B studies
   C interests
   D subjects
4 A completed
   B finished
   C graduated
   D studied
5 A peculiar
   B general
   C individual
   D particular
6 A big
   B extreme
   C high
   D expensive
7 A level
   B proficiency
   C grade
   D stage
8 A pass
   B consider
   C agree
   D regard

C Now write your own letter of application for a scholarship in 120–180 words, using the letter as a model.

Dear Mr. Hill,

  With (1)_____ to your advertisement in the Educational Gazette, I would like to (2)_____ for one of the scholarships your Trust is offering to students who wish to continue their (3)_____ at a British university.

  I am 22 years old and have just (4)_____ in English Philology from the Complutense University in Madrid, Spain. I am very interested in doing a Master's degree in English Literature. My (5)_____ interest is the English playwright Arnold Wesker. However, it is almost impossible for me to study Wesker here in Spain, as he is not very well known. I would really need to come to Britain. Unfortunately, the (6)_____ cost of university fees in your country makes that almost impossible. I would also be living away from home. My parents could contribute something towards my keep but that is all.

  My (7)_____ of English is good. I passed the Cambridge First Certificate examination last year with grade A.
I hope you will (8)_____ my application.

  Yours sincerely,

  Carmen Moreno

EXAM TIP

Remember to include relevant personal information and say how you would benefit if your application was successful.

14 Cause and effect

Reading

1 Before you read

Before you read the text opposite, think about how **you** prepare for examinations. Note down a few techniques you find helpful.

_____

_____

_____

2 Reading

Now read the text quickly. Does the writer mention any of the techniques you noted?

3 Comprehension

Choose the most suitable heading from this list for each paragraph of the text. Write the headings above the correct paragraphs and the paragraph numbers next to the appropriate headings. An example is given. There is one extra heading.

A STAY CALM ____

B BE ORGANIZED ____

C VARY THE WAY YOU REVISE ____

D DON'T WASTE ANY TIME ____

E REMEMBERING THE DIFFICULT BITS ____

F GET SOME SLEEP ____

G WRITE DOWN THE MAIN POINTS ____

H REWARD YOURSELF ____

I SET YOURSELF TARGETS _0_

EXAM TIP

Don't leave any answers blank. If you don't know, make sensible guesses.

HOT TIPS for Staying Cool at Exam Time

0 SET YOURSELF TARGETS

It's always good to know what you're aiming for, so that you know if and when you get there. By having an aim for each week, or even each day, it will help you check your progress and show you if you need to change your plans.

1

Rather than having to work through masses of notes every time you revise something, try noting down things you want to remember on a piece of paper. It doesn't seem as much to learn that way, but it makes sure you don't miss out anything important. Once you've learnt the main points, rewrite them on another piece of paper without looking at your notes.

2

'If you don't know it by now, you'll never learn it for tomorrow.' Everybody says it, but it's probably true. Don't stay up all night studying. You'd be better going to bed at a reasonable time, so that you can wake up fresh and alert on exam day.

3

There's nothing worse than being disorganised. If you have a plan and stick to it, you won't end up cramming all your revision into the last few hours! Make a list of your exams and what you need to learn beforehand, and then draw up a timetable covering all the topics. You can then work out what you need to do on a weekly basis and when you are going to do it.

4

When you reach each of your targets, give yourself a treat – you deserve it! It could be a drink, a short break to watch your favourite TV programme, a phone call to a friend – anything you enjoy. Test yourself, from time to time, on a topic and if you do well, give yourself a special treat based on how well you have done.

5

By now you will probably have discovered the method of revision which suits you best. But every now and then it might be helpful to try a different method. You could try working with a group of friends, or using a different book which covers things from a new angle. Whatever it is, just try something different occasionally.

6

Some things are almost impossible to remember, so you may need to do something unusual to help you remember. Try writing them down in large letters and bright colours and sticking them on the fridge, on a mirror or on the bathroom door. Try recording them on to a cassette and keep playing it back to yourself – on a personal stereo if you've got one!

7

Not too many people like exams and most of us get nervous. But if you've followed your plan and put the effort into revising, then there is not need to worry or panic. Hopefully these tips will have helped you. Give it your best shot – that's all that anyone can expect of you.

4 Prepositions

Fill the gaps in these sentences with an appropriate preposition. There are similar phrases or sentences in the text.

1 Rosy is aiming _____ a high grade in her exams.

2 It's going take me several weeks to work _____ this grammar book.

3 Write your name and address _____ this piece of paper.

4 I usually wake up very early _____ exam days.

5 Once you've made your decision, you should stick _____ it.

6 To keep fit you should exercise _____ a daily basis.

7 Write your name _____ capital letters.

8 Teenagers often stick photos of pop stars _____ their bedroom walls.

9 Why don't you try to see things _____ my angle for a change.

10 We recorded the concert _____ cassette.

Grammar

1 Cause and effect

➤ Grammar reference, Student's Book, page 214

Match a cause from the list on the left with an effect from the list on the right. Then write sentences using one of the verbs or verb phrases below. You may have to add extra words of your own. An example is given.

to result in   to cause   to make someone + adjective
to make someone + verb

Cause	Effect
1 Heavy traffic	serious accidents
2 Overwork	fit
3 Exercise	deafness
4 Eating too much sugar	air pollution
5 Dangerous driving	heart disease
6 Smoking	dance
7 African music	toothache
8 Holidays	tiredness and stress
9 Listening to too much loud music	relax

Example   1   Heavy traffic causes air pollution.

2 Purpose

Find a suitable answer (a–h) to each of these questions (1–8) and then write the answer in full using one of the purpose expressions below. An example is given.

in order to   so as to   so that   to + clause

Questions
1 Why do people buy new clothes?
2 Why do some people have winter holidays?
3 Why do people watch the news on TV?
4 Why do motorcyclists wear helmets?
5 Why do some young people start smoking?
6 Why do spiders make webs?
7 Why do some people go to university?
8 Why do some people have large dogs as pets?

Answers
a find out what's happening in the world
b look fashionable
c be like other people of their age
d protect their heads
e improve chances of getting a good job
f catch their food
g protect their homes against burglars
h learn to ski

Example   1   People buy new clothes *in order to / so as to* look fashionable.

3 *Have / get something done*

➤ Grammar reference, Student's Book, page 214

Match a word from 1–8 with something that is done by that person or in that place. Then make sentences of using all the information and the verb in brackets. You may have to change the words you are given or add new ones. An example is given.

1 hairdresser's	vaccinate dogs (have)
2 optician's	do annual accounts (have)
3 dentist's	service cars (get)
4 doctor's	test eyes (have)
5 vet's	design ncw houses (have)
6 garage	cut hair (get)
7 architect	take out teeth (have)
8 accountant	take blood pressure (have)

Example

1 Tomorrow *I'm going to the hairdresser's to get my hair cut.*

2 Yesterday _____

3 This afternoon _____

4 Last week _____

5 Next Saturday _____

6 The day before yesterday _____

7 Last year _____

8 Next week _____

4 Use of English

Most of the lines in this text contain an unnecessary word. A few of the lines are correct. Read the text carefully, find the extra words and mark them. Tick any lines that are correct. Two examples are given.

Music drives men round the bend too fast

0	Loud music, bad moods and friends who <u>are</u> expect
00	dangerous or exciting driving, all cause young male ✓
1	motorists to drive badly, a report has warned out
2	recently. Some of 17–24-year-olds believe that they
3	are safe drivers but when they are quite obviously
4	not. Consequently, road safety campaigns have a little
5	effect because young men do not realize that they
6	are actually been directed at them.
7	The report, from the Automobile Association
8	Foundation for Road Safety Research found that loud,
9	in-car music can have affect driving abilities. Bad
10	moods which could also cause speeding. One motorist
11	even admitted to that he drove like a complete
12	madman when he was fed up. Many unsafe drivers said
13	friends expected them to be drive riskily, and nearly
14	all young drivers thought the media was generally
15	showed the cars in an over-safe and unrealistic light.

5 Use of English

A Is there a definite link between being tired and run down and the chances of catching a cold? Read the text quickly to find the answer.

B Now read the text more carefully and fill each gap with one suitable word.

This tale is not to be sniffed at

You've probably heard someone say that the reason you caught a cold was that you were 'run down'. People generally accept (1)_____ if you are under pressure or run down you are more likely to get ill. But is this really true (2)_____ is it just an old wives' tale?

The problem with old sayings like this is that it's often difficult to prove whether they are true or not. For example, if you ask people with colds (3)_____ they are feeling run down, they are almost certain (4)_____ say yes. People without colds are more likely to say no. So, (5)_____ do you tell if it's the cold that is making them feel run down or the fact that they are run down that is making them more likely to catch a cold? Now (6)_____ seems there is a scientific answer to this question. And the answer is yes – if you are run down or under stress, you **are** more likely to catch a cold.

Scientists at the Common Cold Research Centre ran (7)_____ series of tests. They got volunteers without colds to attend the centre, (8)_____ they were first given a questionnaire to complete. The questions measured the amount of stress (9)_____ volunteer was under.

The volunteers (10)_____ then deliberately infected with a cold virus and left to see whether they developed a cold. After many people (11)_____ been tested, the researchers looked for a link between the measured stress level and the chances (12)_____ catching a cold. They found that the higher the stress, (13)_____ more likely the person was to catch a cold.

At the moment it (14)_____ not known why stress makes someone more likely to become ill, but now that the link (15)_____ been found, researchers might be able to investigate further. They may even find different ways of combating disease.

Vocabulary

1 People and places in education

➤ Vocabulary reference, Student's Book, page 214

Complete this puzzle with 'education' words which fit the definitions.
1 A child at school.
2 The person in charge of a school is the _____ teacher.
3 After primary school children go to _____ school.
4 A child between the ages of five and seven goes to an _____ school.
5 Before primary school children go to _____ school.
6 A school which children live at is a _____ school.
7 A student who has not yet got a degree.
8 A place of higher education such as Oxford and Cambridge.
9 A teacher at the institution in 8.

```
              9
1  _ _ _ _ | | _
2        | | _ _ _
3    _ _ | | _ _ _ _ _
4  _ _ _ | | _ _ _
5    _ _ | | _ _ _ _
6  _ _ _ | | _ _ _ _
7   _ _ | | _ _ _ _ _ _ _
8  _ _ _ | | _ _ _
```

2 Health

➤ Vocabulary reference, Student's Book, page 214

Which people and places are being described? One or two vowels for each word are given to help you.

1 special doctor who does operations _ U _ _ _ O _
2 where operations are done (two words)
   O _ _ _ _ _ I _ _   _ _ E _ _ _ E
3 nurse who specializes in helping women when they give birth to babies _ I _ _ I _ _
4 someone who is being treated by a doctor or a dentist _ A _ _ E _ _
5 separate part or room of a hospital, where people stay or sleep _ A _ _
6 place where a doctor or dentist sees people with problems _ U _ _ E _ _

3 Use of English

Read this text which gives basic medical advice. Use the word in capital letters to form a word which fits in the space.

Children with high temperatures

A high temperature occurs (1)_____ even with very mild (2)_____. In small children it is important to stop the temperature rising too (3)_____. The best (4)_____ is a spoonful of paracetamol syrup which you can buy from any chemist, without a (5)_____ from your doctor.

If children are still hot, they should be (6)_____ sponged with tepid water. If the temperature does not come down and the child still appears (7)_____, you should contact your doctor (8)_____.

1 COMMON	5 PRESCRIBE
2 INFECT	6 GENTLE
3 QUICK	7 WELL
4 TREAT	8 IMMEDIATE

4 Phrasal verbs

Decide whether the following statements, which include three-part phrasal verbs, are true or false.

1 If you *put up with* someone, you give them a place to sleep. _____
2 People who are overweight should *cut down on* fatty food. _____
3 It's difficult to *go along with* people whose opinions you don't agree with. _____
4 I'm a very sociable person. I *get away with* everyone I meet. _____
5 Imaginative people are always *coming up against* new ideas. _____
6 If you *keep up with* the news, you know what's going on in the world. _____
7 If you *catch up with* someone, you have to ask them to repeat themselves. _____
8 I had to go to the bank because I'd *run out of* money. _____

Writing

Stories ➤Student's Book, page 193

A The text below tells the main events of a story, but does not include descriptions of people, places and objects related to these events. Rewrite the story, adding descriptive language. You should try to add 40-60 more words of your own. There are some questions to help you decide what to add to each paragraph. You can add single words, descriptive phrases or whole sentences to the original.

A visit to the dentist

I woke up on Saturday night with toothache. All day Sunday the pain got worse, so on Monday morning I telephoned the dentist and made an appointment.

I arrived at the surgery fifteen minutes early. There was nobody else in the waiting room and there were no magazines to read. Time passed slowly.

Eventually my name was called and I went in. Mr Parbury asked me to sit down. He examined me and said that one of my teeth would have to come out. He gave me an injection, took out the tooth and ten minutes later I left the surgery.

Questions

Paragraph 1
- How did you feel when you woke up on Saturday night?
- How did you spend Sunday?

_____

_____

_____

_____

_____

Paragraph 2
- What was the atmosphere in the waiting room like?
- How did you feel as you were waiting?

_____

_____

_____

_____

Paragraph 3
- What did the dentist look like?
- How did he behave towards you?
- How did you feel as you left the surgery?

_____

_____

_____

_____

_____

B You are going to write your own story in answer to this question.

An English language magazine is running a competition to find the best 'It happened to me' story. According to the rules, you must begin or end your story with the words
Doctors are wonderful people.

Here are some ideas to think about.

1 Is there a real occasion that you can remember when you or someone you know was helped by a doctor? If not, invent one.
2 Write down the main sequence of events.
3 Try to picture the people, places and objects involved in your story. Make a few more notes.

C Write your story in 120–180 words, making sure you include descriptions as well as saying what happened. Remember, you are aiming to make your story interesting to the reader.

EXAM TIP

Always leave time to check your writing carefully. Look at the Editing Checklist on page 189 of the Student's Book.

This section gives you extra practice in the grammar and vocabulary covered in Units 13 and 14. Before you begin, remind yourself of this language by looking at the Student's Book units and the reference sections.
➤ Grammar reference, pages 213–214
➤ Vocabulary reference, pages 219

Grammar

1 Verb tenses

Fill the gaps in the following sentences with the correct form of the verbs in brackets and including any other words given.

1 When Michelle lived in Italy, she _____(always/have) dinner at 9 p.m.

2 Can you be at the station to meet us? We _____(travel) on the 10 a.m. train, which _____(arrive) in Edinburgh at 15.30.

3 I hate _____(wait) for buses. You _____(wait) for ages and then three _____(come) at the same time.

4 John was exhausted because he _____(work) in the garden all day.

5 I _____(not be) at work tomorrow. I'm taking the day off.

6 On their next anniversary Doris and Fred _____(be) married for 40 years.

7 Did you remember _____(send) your Aunt Mary a card when you _____(be) on holiday?

8 Just think! This time tomorrow we _____(lie) on a beach in the Caribbean.

9 Sorry. I didn't mean _____(stand) on your foot.

10 I feel a bit dizzy. I think I _____(faint).

2 Key word transformations

Complete the second sentence using the word given.

1 They weren't able to finish the project on time. **succeed**
They _____ the project on time.

2 Can you read music? **know**
Do _____ read music?

3 I put my ear to the door in order to hear what they were saying. **so**
I put my ear to the door _____ what they were saying.

4 Too much stress can cause illness, according to medical experts. **make**
Too much stress _____, according to medical experts.

5 You needn't be there before 10 o'clock. **have**
You _____ there before 10 o'clock.

6 A mechanic repaired Joe's car. **fixed**
Joe _____ a mechanic.

7 If you ate less chocolate you might have fewer spots. **much**
If you _____ chocolate you might have fewer spots.

8 It was the worst hotel we'd ever stayed at. **such**
We had _____ bad hotel before.

9 Accommodation is dearer than it used to be. **as**
Accommodation _____ it used to be.

10 I would like to apply for the job. **interested**
I _____ for the job.

3 Correct forms

Choose the correct form from the two choices given.

1 Norman Wisdom is so silly he makes me *laugh / to laugh*.

2 I really must *get repaired my shoes / get my shoes repaired*.

3 He ate a big breakfast *so not to / so that he wouldn't* feel hungry in the middle of the exam.

4 In order *don't / not to* get burnt I only sunbathed for a short time.

5 Don't tell anyone, *will / do* you?

6 There was more than *food enough / enough food* for everyone.

7 *In spite / Despite* not being able to speak the language, we *managed / succeeded* to make ourselves understood.

8 Look after your health *unless / otherwise* you'll regret it later.

9 The news *was / were* reported on the one o'clock bulletin.

10 That actress is believed to *had had / have had* seven facelifts.

4 Expressing ability

Fill the gaps in these sentences with *can* or *be able to* in its correct tense. If both are possible, give the more common form.

1 How long _____ play the piano?

2 Scott _____ speak a little Turkish.

3 Before Mick put on weight, he _____ run for a bus without getting out of breath.

4 I expect _____ type faster by the end of the course.

5 I had drunk so much coffee that I _____ fall asleep for ages.

6 If I really wanted to I _____ beat him easily.

7 While the children amused themselves their parents _____ talk uninterrupted.

8 Even if you'd arrived earlier you _____ get a ticket. They sold out almost immediately.

9 Darren _____ put up the tent in 20 minutes without any help from the rest of us.

10 I'm sorry I _____ find out the information you wanted yet. I've just been so busy.

Vocabulary

1 Correct words

Choose the correct word from the two choices given.

1 The doctor told me to *have / take* the medicine three times a day.

2 The nurse *gave / put* me an injection against the flu.

3 The patient was wheeled into the operating *theatre / surgery*.

4 Doctors' *wages / salaries* have increased by less than the rate of inflation.

5 Jack Nicholson *performs / plays* the part of a villain in the film.

6 Sue got married *to / with* her boyfriend of ten years last weekend.

7 Taylor *shot / scored* his third goal of the season during Saturday's match.

8 I *go / practise* skiing in the winter.

9 My mother is above *medium / average* height.

10 *Packet / Package* holidays are the most popular kind of holiday nowadays.

2 Word building

A Fill in the missing words, according to the information given in brackets.

1 employ (verb)   _____ (negative noun)

2 encourage (verb)   _____ (negative verb)

3 hesitate (verb)   _____ (noun)

4 capable (adjective) _____ (noun)

5 sympathize (verb)   _____ (noun)

6 separate (verb)   _____ (noun)

7 invest (verb)   _____ (noun)

8 apply (verb)   _____ (two nouns)

9 mystery (noun)   _____ (adjective)

10 ill (adjective)   _____ (noun)

B Now complete these sentences with an appropriate word from the ones you have given above. Use each word once only.

1 There is no cure for mental _____, only treatment.

2 Putting your money in stocks and shares is a risky _____.

3 I accepted his offer without _____. It was more money than I had expected.

4 A _____ object rather like a UFO was seen in the district.

5 The government will probably lose the next election because of the high rate of _____ .

6 After a two-year _____, divorce is automatic.

7 I have no _____ for him. He deserves to go to prison.

8 People have different _____ for learning foreign languages.

9 Although both _____ were good, we decided on the one with more experience.

10 I don't want to _____ you from becoming a nurse, but the hours are long and the pay isn't good.

➤

3 Phrasal verbs

Fill the gaps with a phrasal verb in the correct tense made up of a verb and a particle from the lists below. Each particle should be used twice.

Verbs   go   bring   pay
Particles   back   off   on   out   up

1 I ageed _____ the loan in monthly instalments over two years.

2 You can borrow my bike as long as you _____ it _____ by five o'clock. I need it myself this evening.

3 I'm sure this milk _____. It smells funny.

4 What _____? Why is everyone shouting?

5 I'll lend you the money on condition that you _____ it _____.

6 In my opinion, your headaches _____ by stress.

7 I didn't want _____ the topic. It was Malcolm who started asking me about it.

8 Have you seen that awful building they _____ on the corner of Bridge Street?

9 If you don't put more wood on the fire it _____.

10 Apparently they _____ a new low-calorie fizzy drink next month.

You are now ready to do Progress test 4.

Answer Key

Unit 1

Reading

3 Comprehension
1 C *...is said to be Europe's last remaining cannonball*
2 B *...injury to the public*
3 C *...he had to teach me how to take over his act*
4 D *...the essential first step is to line the gun up correctly.*
5 B *...For his next stunt ... a bag over his head*
6 B (general question)

4 Vocabulary
A 1 to   2 for   3 at   4 at   5 on   6 to
B 2 which is going to miss the target
3 while flying / while in the air
4 with two barrels
5 likely to succeed in the future

Grammar

1 Missing prepositions
1 from   2 in   3 from / off   4 in / at
5 in   6 of   7 after

2 Use of English
A John West is the organizer of the bridge-swinging events.
He tells jumpers what to do and controls the rope.
B 1 down   2 bit   3 how
4 yourself   5 not   6 when
7 which   8 enough   9 few
10 to   11 because 12 It
13 as   14 was   15 never

3 Odd one out
1 b is different; a and c refer to present habits
2 c is different; a and b refer to past habits
3 a is different; b and c refer to present habits
4 a is different; b and c refer to a current situation
5 b is different; a and c refer to present habits (b refers to a specific future event)

4 Habitual actions
1 used   2 tend   3 keeps
4 will   5 would   6 tend
7 keep   8 used

Vocabulary

1 Wordsearch

```
P S U B U R B A L T
O H O A U R B A N O
R Y E L L A V N I S
T I B U N G A L O W
O S S B J P F E L I
H B E D S I T C A E
P I N E D R A G R T
E S L A R W E D U P
E T B L D R P L R M
R E P A R C S Y K S
```

2 Overheard remarks
1 greengrocer's shop
2 airport information desk / travel agent's
3 chemist's shop
4 station (train or bus)
5 stationer's shop
6 butcher's shop
7 post office
8 fishmonger's / fish shop / fish and chip shop

3 Jumbled words
1 town hall 2 detached   3 storeys
4 cathedral 5 railway station 6 department store
7 region   8 stream   9 cliff
10 shore

---

4 Phrasal verbs
A 1 d   2 e   3 a   4 b   5 f   6 c
B 1   pick (it) up   2   grow up
3   is going on   4   settle down
5   turned into   6   get through

Writing

A, B
Punctuated and paragraphed text:

Madhu's Brilliant is an Indian restaurant in Southall, an area of London which someone once called "Britain's best-known Asian suburb". It is run by the younger members of the Anand family, whose father, Madhu, started the original restaurant.

It is a glass-fronted building on Southall's lively South Road. Downstairs is brownish and darker, upstairs is blue and white with a bar and a set of tables.

We started our meal with alu gobi, which is potatoes and cauliflower in a sauce of tomato and yoghurt, and then for our main course, we had chicken and prawn curry. We finished off with kulfi, which is a pistachio-flavoured Indian ice-cream. Everything was expertly prepared and tasted delicious.

The cooking at the Brilliant, as is often the case in above average Indian restaurants, comes from one region, in this case the Punjab. I would strongly recommend going to the Brilliant with a few friends to get the benefit of ordering a wider range of dishes from the menu.

Unit 2

Reading

3 Comprehension
1 C *What he didn't know ... - he* = the American futurologist
2 H
3 A *...this won't be the only norm any more. It will simply be one of a number of choices...*
4 F *Offices too will go electronic... too* = in addition to factories
5 B *This would make it possible ... This* = travelling at 15,000 kph
6 E *They'll be fitted with ... They* = cars
7 D

4 Vocabulary
A 2 leisure activities
3 multi-option society
4 head office
5 body panels
6 three-dimensional image
B 1 from   2 on   3 in   4 at
5 with   6 to   7 for

Grammar

1 Use of English
A Statement 3
B 1 what   2 the   3 it   4 The
5 the   6 about   7 as   8 too
9 how   10 by   11 the   12 at

2 Future
A 1 I'm going to go to Australia for my holiday next year.
2 I'm meeting my sister this evening.
3 At this time tomorrow I'll be walking to school.
4 It's going to snow very soon.
5 My train leaves at 7.15 in the morning.
6 After my exams have finished, I'm going to travel round the world on a motorbike.
7 The price of food will (almost certainly / probably) go up next year.
8 My plane lands at 11.15 at night.
B 2 **I'm going to pass** my driving test...
3 ...**I'll answer** it.
4 Correct

---

5 ...**we'll finish / we're going to** finish all the food
6 Correct; also acceptable: **is starting** in five minutes
7 I'm sure someone **will object**
8 What **are you going to do** ...? / What **are you doing** ...?

3 Articles
1 the   2 Ø   3 a   4 the   5 Ø
6 Ø   7 a   8 a   9 Ø   10 the
11 the   12 a   13 an   14 a   15 the
16 a   17 an   18 the

Vocabulary

1 Puzzle

```
1        S H O W E R
2        R A I N F A L L
3 L I G H T N I N G
4 S N O W F L A K E
5        S U N B U R N
6    M I S T O N E
7        F O R E C A S T
8        S U N S H I N E
9    F I N E
```

2 Use of English
A 1 15 October 1987   25 January 1990
2 47
B 1 C   2 D   3 D   4 A   5 B
6 A   7 B   8 A   9 D   10 C

3 Phrasal verbs
1 will put up taxes
2 get through all our money
3 turn into a really nice day
4 to put you up for the night
5 After we break up at the end of the week...
6 settled down again
7 to break up the meeting

Writing

Formal and informal styles
A 1 c   2 e   3   4 a
5 b   6   7 d
B The texts are given in brackets after the formal words:
2 inform (a)
3 receive (a)
4 All items (b)
5 your chosen items (b)
6 at your earliest convenience (c)
7 additional charges (d)
8 required documents (e)

Unit 3

Reading

3 Comprehension
1 A *Their constant barking interrupts my sleep.*
2 B *Noise heads the list*
3 D *The Bristol-based charity*
4 B *Buyers can be put off by the external appearance of neighbouring houses.*
5 C
6 D *when I spotted the dogs I had my doubts; they bark all night; another lucky escape.*
7 C

4 Vocabulary
1 get away   2 stress and strain   3 crockery
4 disputes   5 widespread   6 put off
7 bother

5 Text references
1 The dogs
2 Taking legal action
3 The 60 regional groups
4 The alsatians

6 Reading between the lines

1 They would always be doing repairs and they would make a lot of noise with their hammers and electric drills.
2 In the first place, possibly because he wanted his house to look different. Later on, possibly because he wanted to make a point.
3 Because if they had difficult neighbours, they would never sell their houses.

Grammar

1 Gerunds and infinitives

A 1 to get, to wish
2 wasting; to get
3 to inform
4 to visit; travelling
5 to get up; to set
6 leaving
7 smoking; having
8 wondering; to afford; to run
9 to meet; to hear
10 being; having

B 1 for; on
2 at
3 with; about
4 at
5 for
6 about
7 of
8 on
9 in
10 at; in

2 Use of English

2 went on working
3 you regret not going / you regret not having gone
4 didn't mean to insult
5 is good at adding up
6 not mind if Paul comes / not mind Paul coming
7 noise prevented me (from) hearing
8 be put off by / get put off by

3 Use of English

A Headline 1 would be the most appropriate.

B

1 her
2 the
3 is
4 at
5 was / started / began
6 which
7 a
8 each
9 to
10 me
11 that
12 our / my / his
13 how
14 what
15 has

Vocabulary

1 Use of English

1 accidentally
2 commercial
3 decision
4 shyness
5 amazement
6 confidence
7 marriage
8 depressing
9 publicity
10 successful

2 Wordsearch

1 screen
2 gallery
3 musicians
4 vocalist
5 pit
6 plot
7 conductor
8 row
9 encore
10 aisle
11 rock and roll
12 applaud
13 stage
14 boo

3 Topic vocabulary

1 cloth
2 charcoal
3 clay
4 canvas
5 wool
6 stone
7 plaster
8 paint

4 Phrasal verbs

A 1 increase: put up
2 distract: put off
3 discourage: put off
4 get dressed in, wear: put on
5 provide accommodation for: put up
6 build: put up
7 switch on: put on
8 postpone / delay: put off

B 1 off
2 on
3 up
4 on
5 up
6 off
7 up
8 off

Writing

A Jumbled text
1 a
2 h
3 g
4 c
5 i
6 b
7 f
8 d
9 j
10 e

Complete text:
Are artists born or made? I've often wondered. I don't really know why because, in my case, neither one nor the other seems to be true.

Even when I was a child, I wanted to be an artist. I imagined myself living in an attic room in Paris painting masterpieces. But the nearest I ever got to producing one was the painting-by-numbers Mona Lisa I did when I was twelve.

Then when I was a teenager, I decided to be more realistic. I decided to take up knitting and from the age of sixteen I knitted a sweater for every boy I went out with. Giving someone a sweater which goes down to their knees, I discovered, is a sure way of ending any relationship.

As a university student, I tried pottery but I wasn't any better at that. In the end I was forced to admit that not everyone is born to be artistic.

Unit 4

Reading

3 Comprehension

1 D The word *It* in the sentence following the gap *It also included …* refers to *a note in the kitchen* in sentence D.
2 G The word *They* in sentence G refers to the Schoos.
3 A This is a continuation of what the neighbour Connie Stadelmann said.
4 F The word *She* in sentence F refers to the neighbour.
5 B This sentence continues the sequence of events leading to the arrest of the Schoos.
6 E The fact that the couple *didn't even inquire how their children were* follows on from the phrase *declined to comment* in the sentence before the gap.

4 Vocabulary

1 *they* = the Schoos, the mother and father
2 *their* = the children's
3 *They* = the parents (mother and father)
them = the children
4 *this* = leaving their children while they go away on holiday
5 *which* = this film
6 *they* = the (rest of the) family

B 1 insults
2 onlookers
3 reminder
4 evidence
5 plight
6 trace
7 decline(d)
8 cruelty

C 1 f
2 d (also *footpath* in British English)
3 e
4 i
5 g
6 b
7 a (in British English a *purse* is mainly used for carrying coins)
8 h
9 c

Vocabulary

1 Puzzle

					11							
1			B	O	S	S						
2			P	A	R	T	N	E	R			
3	F	I	A	N	C	E						
4			E	M	P	L	O	Y	E	R		
5			E	M	P	L	O	Y	E	E		
6			C	O	L	L	E	A	G	U	E	
7	A	C	Q	U	A	I	N	T	A	N	C	E
8		D	A	U	G	H	T	E	R			
9				N	E	I	G	H	B	O	U	R
10			G	I	R	L	F	R	I	E	N	D

---

2 Compound nouns

A Note
Dictionaries do not always agree about which words are hyphenated, which are written as one word and which are written as two words. These answers are based on the spelling used in the Oxford 'Wordpower' dictionary.
1 backpack
2 front page (or *front-page* if it used as an adjective)
3 lunch-time
4 lighthouse
5 housework
6 price rise
7 camp-site
8 suitcase
These compounds are also possible: *back page / lunch-pack*

B 1 g
2 b
3 c
4 e
5 h
6 a
7 f
8 d

3 Use of English

1 D
2 A
3 B
4 D
5 A
6 D
7 B
8 A
9 C
10 C
11 A
12 D
13 B
14 B
15 C

4 Phrasal verbs

A 1 up
2 up
3 down
4 down
5 up
6 up
7 up
8 down

B 1 False: *take to* = to like quickly
2 False: should be *put off*
3 True
4 True
5 True
6 False: *get through* = spend everything
7 False: *put off* = postpone, not do

Grammar

1 Use of English

1 most
2 to (them)
3 the
4 are
5 √
6 for
7 √
8 into
9 √
10 have
11 with
12 a
13 being
14 that
15 of

2 Comparative adjectives and adverbs

1 further
2 better
3 more informally
4 more friendly
5 harder
6 hotter
7 worse
8 faster

3 Use of English

1 more you read
2 an enjoyable holiday (that)
3 the sooner the
4 are less expensive
5 more and more dangerous
6 surprising there were so many
7 a bit warmer / hotter than
8 as / so safe as

Writing

A Correct order of paragraphs: C, E, B, A, D
The letter is a reply to the advertisement beginning COSY COTTAGES.

B 1 Topics of paragraphs:
1 C - introduction stating the purpose of the letter
2 E - information about group and their needs
3 B - request for price details
4 A - an additional point about preferred location
5 D - conclusion, asking for quick reply

2 *I am now writing for further details* (C)
(we) would be most grateful if you could let us know (E)
Please could you also let us have details (B)
Are there reductions… (B)
…please could you send this information (D)

3 The letter contains these features of formal letters:
• Long sentences (e.g. paragraph C)
• Long verb forms (e.g. *We would prefer...*)
• Special polite phrases (e.g. *… and would be most grateful if*)

Revision 1

Grammar

1 Correct forms

1 losing	2 to have	3 Shall
4 the	5 the	6 walking
7 worrying	8 wishing	9 as
10 such		

2 Verb tenses

1 drinks	2 will / 'll be
3 is going to work	4 will / 'll do
5 leaves	6 criticizing
7 are spending	8 will have been living
9 will / 'll be doing	
10 went	

3 Key word transformations

1 was so cold
2 he tends to fall
3 the more difficult it was
4 I will have finished
5 about to lose
6 regret sending you that letter
7 used to live in Bristol
8 the oldest (one)
9 responsible for stealing
10 will have been working

Vocabulary

1 Definitions

1 detached	2 acquaintance	3 stress
4 audience	5 interval	6 basement
7 lightning	8 common sense	9 channel
10 clay		

2 Word building

1 improve	2 expectation	3 manage
4 performance	5 education	6 reside
7 marriage	8 decide	9 amazement
10 applaud		

3 Phrasal verbs

A

1 f	2 j	3 h	4 b	5 e
6 d	7 c	8 g	9 a	10 i

B

1 put (me) off	2 picked (it) up
3 settled down	4 puts up
5 grew up	6 put on
7 turned into	8 got through
9 take up	10 is going on

Unit 5

Reading

1 Before you read

1 False: athletes who compete in field sports like the discus and shot putt will be smaller and less strong because they won't take drugs.
2 False: drugs controls will be tightened.
3 False: both are important but diet after a race is especially important.
4 False: they help prevent injury and are more comfortable to run in but don't help athletes run faster.
5 False: the angle of take-off is the most important factor.

3 Comprehension

1 D   2 A   3 B   4 F   5 E   6 C

4 Vocabulary

A

1 h	2 c	3 f	4 b	5 g	6 e
7 a	8 d			

B

1 battle   2 flexible   3 genuine
4 predicts / predicted / has predicted
5 neglect   6 motto   7 vital   8 elusive

Grammar

1 Past tenses

A

1 was driving	2 was raining
3 was beginning	4 saw
5 opened	6 asked

7 got in	8 was making / made
9 Have / Had you been waiting	
10 shook	11 tried
12 gave	13 noticed
14 realized	15 was
16 drove off	17 reached
18 had left	19 picked (it) up
20 had had	

B
1 went; wasn't / hadn't been; fell; got married
2 Haven't you finished;'ve been doing;'ve done
3 said; got back; couldn't; wrote / had written down
4 had put; rang; thought; rushed; stopped / had stopped; reached
5 've forgotten
6 has / had; was wearing; drove off
7 had covered; went
8 thought / was thinking; had picked up; started; was
9 've been peeling
10 was sitting; realized I had left

2 Use of English

A The text is about a new sport (the idea of Richard Turner).

B

1 of	2 to	3 as	4 it
5 such	6 has	7 like	8 are
9 which	10 able	11 what	12 so
13 is	14 and	15 will	

Vocabulary

1 Use of English

1 injuries	2 accidentally	3 failure
4 Luckily	5 landing	6 flight
7 inexperienced	8 investigation	9 safety
10 emotional		

2 Topic vocabulary

1 boxing   2 ice-hockey   3 weightlifting
4 golf

3 Crossword

	¹R	A	C	²I	N	G	³	⁴	⁵R
	A		⁶A	C	E		O		E
⁷S	C	O	R	E			A		F
	K		E		S		L		E
⁸N	E	⁹T		K		¹⁰T		R
I		¹¹E	N	A		¹²R	A	C	E
L		¹¹P	A	¹⁴S	T	I	C	K	E
	A	M		E	E		K		
	S		¹⁵S	A	D	D	L	E	
	¹⁶S	E	R	V	E		E		

4 Phrasal verbs

1 off	2 off	3 up	4 up	5 off
6 away	7 to			

Writing

Stories

A Punctuated story

An embarrassing incident
One summer job I had as a student was in a rather exclusive restaurant in Glasgow. On this particular day we were expecting forty members of a football team for lunch. I was given the job of peeling the potatoes.

I thought I was managing quite well with my small knife until the owner appeared to see how I was getting on. She was amazed that I was using a knife and asked why I wasn't using the potato peeler. I had no idea what a potato peeler was so she led me into a small room behind the main kitchen. There on the table was a small machine rather like the rubbish bins some people have in

their bathrooms. She explained, as if to a small child, that I only had to put the potatoes in, close the lid and press the button.

When she came back ten minutes later, I told her I thought it was quicker to do them by hand. She asked what I meant. 'Well they aren't ready yet,' I replied. You can imagine how I felt when she lifted the lid and took out the potatoes the size of peas. The potato peeler was not automatic.

B Jumbled story

1 c f i	2 g a e	3 h b d

Unit 6

Reading

3 Comprehension

1 D ... *we saw her off at the airport in August. / As we said our goodbyes...*
2 G *During that first year...* refers to the first period of time she was away from home
3 A ... *she **returned** to the US. / Although we had been preparing for her **return**...*
4 F *I feel they have bought her. / **This** is more than just the pain...*
5 B ... *a permanent member of our family. / ...taking on **this** parental responsibility...*
6 C ... *persuaded by the **family** here. / **This family** has broken*

4 Vocabulary

1 to board	2 hostile	3 anxious
4 primary	5 culture shock	6 permanent

Grammar

1 Conditional sentences

A

1 we'll go	2 it takes
3 wouldn't look	4 I'll tell
5 wouldn't have stopped	6 is
7 wouldn't have got	8 hasn't got
9 I'll phone	10 practised

B
1 If Sue hadn't been ill, she would have gone to the party.
2 If there was a theatre in my town, I would go more often.
3 If Jeff hadn't broken his leg, he would have played football.
4 If my mother wasn't afraid of water, she would go swimming.
5 If I had £100,000 to spare, I'd like to buy a yacht.
6 If it had snowed, we could have gone skiing.
7 If he had been looking where he was going, he wouldn't have walked into the road sign.
8 If I knew her address, I could send her a postcard.

2 Use of English

1 if you don't tell   2 because you had left
3 if I had brought   4 to call in if you
5 so I can't drive   6 crash might not have been
7 Unless somebody (someone) complains / makes a complaint
8 we may get

3 Use of English

A 3

B

1 in	2 her	3 for	4 at	5 to
6 who ('who' is more appropriate than 'which' because the spider has a human name)				
7 by	8 every	9 of	10 are	11 that
12 If	13 it / this / that	14 their	15 was	

Vocabulary

1 Body idioms

1 finger	2 back	3 hair
4 feet	5 arm	6 head
7 neck	8 tongue	

2 Phrasal verbs

A

1 discover = find out   2 separated = split up
3 fainted = passed out   4 continue = carry on
5 reveal = give away   6 met = bumped into

B Matching

1 c let them down   2 h die out
3 a picking me up   4 f take on
5 b make up   6 e thrown away
7 d set off   8 g carrying out /
                        going to carry out

3 Use of English

A 1 a snake / python   2 a car and a lorry
B 1 C   2 B   3 A   4 A   5 A
     6 C   7 D   8 B   9 C   10 D

Writing

Reports

A Sub-headings
1 C   2 B   3 G   4 A   5 E

B Phrases
1 g   2 c   3 e
4 f - 'report' is used as a verb here
5 h   6 b   7 a   8 d

Unit 7

Reading

1 Before you read

A 1   The graduate is working in a fast-food restaurant.
    2   Probably because it is the only job they could find.
    3   In Britain it is difficult to find a job, even for well-qualified graduates.

3 Comprehension
1 F   2 A   3 C   4 G   5 E   6 D

4 Vocabulary
a pointless   b compromise
c rewarding   d tricky
e get in touch with   f pros and cons
g first-hand   h colleagues
i compassionate

5 Word building
1 d   2 h   3 a   4 e   5 b
6 g   7 c   8 f

Grammar

1 Relative pronouns
1 , which ... platform 1,
2 Friday, which; when / that / Ø
3 , whose ... collectors,   4 who / that
5 Ø / why   6 where
7 whose; who / that   8 , which ... game,
9 Ø / that   10 Ø / that / which
11 , where   12 , when
13 Ø / that / which   14 , which
15 who / that

2 Use of English
1 the party was rather boring
2 to whom I spoke
3 was quite an easy exam
4 which was a foolish
5 a lot of interest
6 which Jason has bought has
7 the robbers got away in
8 who is particularly good

3 Use of English
1 had   2 of   3 much   4 did
5 for   6 a   7 √   8 of
9 as   10 it   11 who   12 √
13 that   14 what   15 √   16 √

Vocabulary

1 Word building
1 UNSOCIABLE

---

2 IRRESPONSIBLE
3 DISORGANIZED
4 IMPOLITE
5 INSECURE
6 IMPATIENT
7 UNCARING
8 ILLITERATE

2 Jumbled sentences
1 The thief was wearing a mask over his face.
2 Is your hair dyed or is that its natural colour?
3 He is short-sighted so he has to wear glasses.
4 She never wears her hair tied back in a pony tail.
5 My father started going grey when he was only 30. / My father was only 30 when he started going grey.
6 She is so petite that she can wear childrens' clothes.
7 The more you worry, the more wrinkles you get.
8 Karen has long red hair just like her twin sister.

3 Use of English
1 measurements   2 creative   3 pleasure
4 patience   5 demanding   6 comfortable
7 enjoyable   8 variety   9 satisfaction
10 qualifications

4 Phrasal verbs
1 no   2 yes   3 no   4 yes
5 yes   6 no   7 no   8 no
set off: start a journey
break out: escape from prison
take to: begin to like something
let down: fail to do something for someone who was relying on you.
hold up: rob using a gun
give away: give something to someone as a present or because you no longer want it
turn down: decline; not accept
look forward to: await something with pleasure

Writing

Applications

A Three different trips are mentioned: two special projects to west Nepal and the Everest trek. Anyone would be eligible to apply: *John Havens is looking for anyone, male, female, young, old ...*

B Opening sentences
1 reference / regard; advertisement; edition
2 applying; post / position; advertised
3 enquire; places
4 grateful; details

Unit 8

Reading

1 Before you read
You probably answered:
1 a caution
2 five years' imprisonment
3 25 years' imprisonment

2 Reading
The correct answers are:
1 25 years' imprisonment
2 a caution
3 five years' imprisonment

3 Comprehension
1 C   2 B   3 D   4 C   5 E   6 B
7 E   8 B   9 D   10 D   11 A

4 Vocabulary
1 wrappings   2 released
3 a spokesperson   4 a beggar
5 daring   6 incriminating
7 hold-up   8 grab
9 a dare   10 fake
11 provoked   12 a vandal

Grammar

1 Use of English
1 √   2 the   3 √   4 it
5 do   6 yet   7 which   8 so
9 √   10 down   11 √   12 onto
13 √   14 some   15 with

2 Reported speech

A Suggested answers:
1 'Hurry up! We're going to be late!'
2 'Do you think I should wear my red dress or my green one?'
3 'Your black one.' / 'I'd wear your black dress.'
4 'I can't. It's at the dry-cleaner's.'
5 'Look I don't care what you wear but if we're late I might lose my job!'

B Suggested answers:
1 He added that Pete and John were coming so there would be some people there that she knew. Delia said (that) she would love to go and asked what time it started. Paul replied that it started at about ten but that she could come when she liked.
2 Delia told Angie (that) she had been invited to Paul's party. Angie asked when it was. Delia replied that it was on Saturday / the following Saturday adding that she didn't want to go but hadn't been able to decline / turn down the invitation. Angie suggested phoning Paul / that she should phone Paul / that she phoned Paul on the Saturday to say that she didn't feel well.
3 When Delia asked John if he was going to Paul's party, John said (that) he didn't think so. He had gone the previous year / the year before / last year and it had been really boring. He asked Delia if she was going.
4 Paul's mother warned Paul not to make too much noise adding that she didn't want any complaints from the neighbours. Paul promised not to / that he wouldn't.
5 Pete asked Delia why she hadn't gone to Paul's party. Delia replied that she hadn't gone because everyone had said it would be boring. Pete said (that) he had really enjoyed it and that it hadn't finished until after 4. He added that Angie and John had been there.

C
1 John's mother told him not to speak with his mouth full.
2 Laura's mother reminded her to get her father a birthday present.
3 The man warned me / us etc not to drink the water (because it was dirty.)
4 Susie suggested trying the new Chinese restaurant in King Street.
5 David insisted on paying.
6 The managing director asked Miss Smith to retype the letter.

3 Use of English
1 is   2 them   3 about   4 one
5 and   6 so   7 if   8 few
9 which / that   10 it   11 before
12 an   13 for   14 you   15 as

Vocabulary

1 Use of English
1 mysteries   2 aggressive   3 success
4 inability   5 reflecting   6 absence
7 selfish   8 discomfort
9 pleasure   10 convenience

2 Phrasal verbs
1 went (carefully) through
2 go over
3 didn't go with
4 has gone out
5 to go back
6 are (always) going off

3 Use of English
1 D   2 B   3 B   4 D   5 B   6 A
7 B   8 D   9 C   10 A   11 A

Writing

Compositions

A

1 In countries where the price of cigarettes is high, financial reasons play an important part in persuading people to stop smoking.
2 Reducing the number of areas where people can smoke should in theory reduce the amount they can smoke. However, it makes some people even more determined to carry on smoking.
3 Many people, particularly young people, start smoking because of peer pressure. It would be difficult to be the only smoker in a group for the same reasons.
4 Although most people would not want to run the risk of breaking the law and having a criminal record, they would regard it as interfering with their civil liberties.

B Linking ideas

1 In addition; and; which
2 so; because
3 One of the advantages; if
The correct order of the sentences is: 3 2 1.

Revision 2

Grammar

1 Verb tenses

1 had already closed; arrived
2 have been trying   3 arrived; started
4 lived / was living; got 5 have ever seen
6 was driving; ran out   7 haven't invited
8 had   9 went; thought
10 was listening

2 Correct forms

1 hurry   2 oldest   3 told; talking
4 has been   5 had worn   6 Having slept
7 which   8 done   9 going
10 quite a

3 Key word transformations

1 went on searching / looking
2 disturb me unless
3 is such a good dancer
4 find out the truth until
5 know if Marie had had
6 were fewer people / were not as many people
7 don't usually answer
8 after he (had) switched off / when he had switched off
9 told him not to speak
10 which he grew up

Vocabulary

1 Phrasal verbs

1 down   2 up   3 after
4 off   5 away   6 to
7 up with   8 over; back 9 down
10 off

2 Word building

A

1 indecisive   2 careless
3 uncreative   4 disorganized
5 unsociable   6 inexperienced
7 unreliable   8 illegal
9 uneducated   10 unbelievable

B

1 illegal   2 careless
3 inexperienced   4 disorganized
5 unreliable   6 indecisive
7 uneducated   8 unbelievable
9 unsociable   10 Uncreative

Unit 9

Reading

3 Comprehension

1F *original costumes*
2 / 3A *animals from all over the world*; H *birds from all over the globe*
4 / 5A *adventure playground*; H *play area*
6 / 7B; E *Bourton-on-the-Water*
8C *agricultural exhibits*
9G *windsurfing, sailing, and water-skiing*
10 / 11 / 12A *a picnicking area*; G - *picnic sites*; H *picnic area*
13 / 14 / 15B *18th century watermill*; D *wool merchant's house*; F *Pump Room*

4 Vocabulary

A

A spacious
B amazing / beautiful
D unique / enchanting
E delightful
F magnificent / beautiful / original / spectacular
G exciting
H newly-created / newly-opened

B Suggested answers:

1 snake / lizard / crocodile / alligator / turtle
2 crab / fish of all kinds / water plants / shellfish of all kinds
3 swing / see-saw / slide / roundabout / play-house / climbing frame
4 oven / sink / washing machine / cupboards / food / cooking equipment

Grammar

1 Suggestions, advice and warnings

1 you ought to call
2 were you I'd
3 should arrange to
4 ought to phone her
5 'd (had) better not
6 (that) you drink less coffee
7 why don't you eat
8 eating chocolate, otherwise you'll

2 Ought to / should / could

1 should / ought to   2 could
3 should / ought to   4 Could
5 should / ought to   6 could
7 should / ought to   8 could

3 Contrasting link words

1 even though / although
2 but
3 In spite of / Despite (less common: Although / Even though)
4 However
5 Although / Even though
6 in spite of / despite

4 Use of English

A 3 - *It's his age - his body's changing...*
B 1 under   2 about   3 one
    4 has   5 for   6 ever
    7 would   8 If / When 9 to
    10 To   11 more   12 as
    13 why   14 that   15 than

Vocabulary

1 Word families

2 space
3 add / additional / additionally
4 complex
5 violent / violently
6 imagination / imagine / imaginative (imaginary / imagined)
7 inclusion / inclusive (included) / inclusively
8 selection (selector) / selective / selectively
9 explain / explanatory
10 recognition / recognized (recognizable) / recognizably

2 Wordsearch

1 air   2 boat   3 road
4 train   5 rail   6 taxi
7 motorway   8 ferry   9 airport
10 plane   11 sea   12 coach
13 station   14 motorbike 15 bike
16 car

3 Use of English

1 crowded   2 natural
3 unspoilt / unspoiled   4 unpolluted
5 expensive   6 comparison
7 exceptionally   8 comfortable
9 friendly   10 relaxation
11 unforgettable

4 Phrasal verbs

A 1 take up   2 bring up   3 put off
    4 take to   5 bring in 6 bring out
    7 put out   8 put up
B 1 brought out   2 put out   3 putting (it) off
    4 put (you) up 5 brought (the matter) up

Writing

Transactional letters

A 1 within five days
    2 for a period of six months
    3 for whatever reason
    4 to discuss the situation
    5 at the head of this letter
    6 to recover the cost

Unit 10

Reading

1 Before you read

All the words listed are in the text with the exception of sky and memory. Note that three words are used in different forms in the text: *disappeared, escaped* and *flying.*

3 Comprehension

1 F   2 A   3 E   4 B   5 C
You do not need to use paragraph D.

4 Vocabulary

A

1 reality / realism 2 terror   3 amazement
4 nation   5 fame   6 beauty

B

1 disappearance   2 indication
3 conviction   4 observation / observer
5 conclusion   6 publication / publisher

Grammar

1 Modal verbs

A 1 Do you have to... / Must you...
    2 must / should
    3 need to / have to
    4 must
    5 had to
    6 should
    7 have to / need to
    8 need to / have to / must / should
B 1 don't have to / don't need to / needn't wear
    2 mustn't drive
    3 needn't / don't need to / don't have to give
    4 didn't need to / didn't have to show
    5 needn't have brought
    6 mustn't forget

7 needn't / don't need to / don't have to worry
8 didn't have to / didn't need to pay

2 Use of English
1 are not allowed to ride
2 leave home early enough
3 smoking is not permitted
4 unless he spends
5 was banned from
6 too young to
7 I needn't / don't need to
8 let me stay
9 goes fast enough for
10 too difficult for

3 Use of English
1 be	2 to (me)	3 much	4 of
5 √	6 am	7 a	8 the
9 to	10 will	11 √	12 a
13 as (, and)	14 √	15 me	

Vocabulary

1 Clothes
A 1 Warm: coat / overcoat / scarf / pullover
(sweater / jumper) / hat / gloves / boots
Dry: raincoat / mackintosh (mac) / hat /
anorak / boots
2 Cool: T-shirt / shorts / sandals / thin blouse
(shirt)
3 Made of leather: shoes / boots / jacket / belt
/ gloves
4 A pair of: boots / glasses / gloves / jeans /
knickers / pants / pyjamas sandals / shoes /
shorts / slippers / socks / swimming trunks
tights / trousers
5 Usually worn by women: blouse / skirt /
dress / frock / bra / knickers / tights /
6 Usually worn by men: shirt / pants /
(swimming) trunks / suit

B 1 belt	b	2 cardigan	h	
3 beret	d	4 anorak	g	
5 slippers	f	6 pyjamas	e	
7 sweater	a	8 scarf	c	

2 Use of English
1 B	2 A	3 B	4 B	5 D	6 C
7 B	8 A	9 A	10 C	11 D	

3 Phrasal verbs
1 looking for	2 have sold out
3 try (it) on	4 take (my coat) off
5 put (it) on	6 wear out

Writing

Articles
A 1 example; topic   2 situation
3 reader; relevant; personal
4 Surprise; strong   5 problem; answer
6 summarize   7 thinking
8 opinion   9 round off

Unit 11

Reading

1 Before you read
A Biosphere 2 is an environmental project in
which scientists are trying to create a closed
ecological system.
B Some possible questions might be:
How did you get involved in the project?
How many other people were there in the
project?
Were there men as well as women?
Did everyone get on?
What did you miss most about the outside world?
Would you go back?

3 Comprehension
A
1 G ... how they had passed the time when they
weren't working.
2 E The diet was quite monotonous.

3 / 4 / 5 B ... enthusiastic about her time ...; C ... her
excitement about the project.; I ... she says, grinning
happily. 'I can't wait!'
6 H And did they get on?
7 A ... school in London; university at Sheffield ...
8 F ... the white potatoes got infected ...
9 / 10 D; F
11 B She is open, friendly, humorous ...
12 C Their return was met with some criticism.

4 Reading between the lines
1 They are accused of being more interested in
making a profit from tourism than the results
of their scientific research.
2 Yes. She spent time thinking about what had
to be done during the day. She is also
responsible for training the next team.

5 Vocabulary
1 very big / enormous
2 practical and strong, not fashionable and
attractive
3 obvious
4 someone who likes getting up early
5 something special and enjoyable
6 a variety / kind
7 with two floors
8 toilets
9 small and unimportant
10 planned / expected

Grammar

1 Use of English
1 a	2 to	3 their / the
4 while / although / though		5 be
6 however	7 is	8 from
9 on	10 this / it	11 there
12 an	13 until / unless	14 have
15 in		

2 Possibilities and probabilities
1 I could / might have misheard
2 she can't be coming
3 I might invite him
4 You must have taken
5 The oven can't have been
6 It must be

3 Eight things you might regret saying!
A Suggested answers:
1 • To a friend, son or daughter.
• The other person wants to learn how to drive
and probably can't find anyone willing.
2 • To a friend or colleague.
• The person who is giving the party is having
problems finding a place to have it.
3 • To friends or colleagues.
• They are in the pub and the speaker is
offering to buy everyone a drink.
4 • To someone who doesn't know them very
well, possibly a prospective boyfriend /
girlfriend.
• The listener is being asked to guess the
speaker's age. The speaker thinks he / she
looks younger than he / she actually is.
5 • To a friend.
• They are going somewhere together
possibly in a hurry and on foot.
6 • To a friend.
• The friend needs some money.
7 • To a friend, son or daughter.
• The other person looks upset.
B
1 Pete wishes he hadn't offered to teach his wife
to drive. They spend the whole lesson shouting
at each other.
2 Katie wishes she hadn't offered to hold the
party at her place. It'll take her days to clean
up the mess.
3 Mr. Brown wishes he hadn't invited everyone
to a drink. They all asked for whisky.
4 Julie wishes she hadn't asked the boy how old
he thought she was. He said 'Sixty'.

5 Andrew wishes he hadn't said he knew a
short-cut. They got completely lost.
6 Bridget wishes she hadn't offered to lend Clare
some money. She still hasn't got it back.
7 Maria wishes she hadn't told Carole to tell her
what was wrong. She spent three hours
listening to her problems.

Vocabulary

1 Use of English
1 difference	2 replaced	3 treatment
4 international	5 operations	6 sight
7 worldwide	8 importance	9 inexperienced
10 latest		

2 Use of English
1 D	2 B	3 A	4 D	5 C
6 A	7 C	8 D	9 B	10 B

3 Puzzle
```
          8
1       A C I D
2   N U C L E A R
3     F E R T I L I Z E R
4     S O L A R
5   W A S T E
6     B O T T L E
7     O I L - S L I C K
```

4 Phrasal verbs
1 come out	2 came across
3 are coming round	4 come up with
5 came round	6 has come up

Writing

The opinion composition
A 1 a toaster   2 a washing machine / spin drier
B 1 so that   2 unless   3 Despite
4 if   5 in order to   6 Although

Unit 12

Reading

2 Reading
1 True: sleepwalkers have been known to drive
cars, ride motorbikes and other complex
activities.
2 False: sleepwalkers usually spend a maximum
of 15 minutes out of bed. People who suffer
from nocturnal blackouts or amnesia spend
much longer out of bed than sleepwalkers.
3 False: the opposite is true.
4 True: sleepwalking seems to be hereditary
5 False: stress and anxiety are believed to be the
major causes.

3 Comprehension
1 G	2 A	3 F	4 C	5 B	6 E

4 Reading between the lines
1 Many of her friends live abroad (international
calls).
2 More men than women are in stressful jobs.
Also men tend to keep their worries to
themselves, whereas women are more likely to
talk about them.
3 When they are away from familiar
surroundings, for example on holiday or
moving to a new house.

5 Vocabulary
1 d	2 i	3 a	4 h	5 g
6 c	7 e	8 b	9 j	10 f

6 Word building
2 anxiety   3 tiredness   4 capabilities
5 behaviour   6 consumption   7 uneventful
8 injuries   9 addictive   10 solution

Grammar

1 Active or passive
1 are employed
2 happened; was hurt
3 were cleaned; were changed
4 was warned; was caught
5 were sent; broke down
6 was given
7 have been made; was taken over
8 hasn't been / wasn't / isn't invited

2 Use of English
1 is (being) taken up by
2 is said to have been
3 ought to be thrown away
4 is thought to be living
5 upset Josie a great / good
6 is expected to open
7 was eventually put out by
8 is believed to have been

3 Use of English
A Six festivals are mentioned: Easter; Swedish spring festival; Hindu festival of Holi; Thai New Year; spring festival in Antigua in Guatemala; Chinese spring festival.

B 1 when 2 however 3 the
4 by 5 are 6 from
7 other 8 which 9 instead
10 with / to 11 ago 12 many / some / other
13 of 14 have 15 for

4 Use of English
1 must 2 the 3 √ 4 most 5 to
6 both 7 √ 8 of 9 it 10 for
11 √ 12 that 13 too 14 are 15 √

Vocabulary

1 Use of English
1 safety 2 unlikely 3 incorrectly
4 attention 5 instructions 6 dangerous
7 harmless 8 favourite 9 completely
10 careful

2 Phrasal verbs
A 1 away f 2 on e
3 down d 4 by b
5 over c 6 out a
B 1 have been brought up / were brought up
2 get out
3 saved up / had saved up / has been saving up
4 to run out
5 hung up
6 took out / has taken out
7 to carry out
8 turned up

3 Word ladder

¹C	O	N	T	A	I	N	E	R
²T	E	N	D	E	R			
³M	I	L	D					
⁴B	A	K	E					
⁵C	R	U	M	B	S			
⁶S	A	V	O	U	R	Y		
⁷M	I	C	R	O	W	A	V	E
⁸G	E	T	-	T	O	G	E	T	H	E	R
⁹O	V	E	R	C	O	O	K	E	D

Writing

Reports
A 1 A friend
2 Her school trip to Madrid
3 Writing a report on the trip for the head teacher

B
Suggested notes:
Journey
Left London by coach Sat. June 8th. Arrived Madrid Sun. June 9th. 11pm. Very long and tiring. Three people sick on coach. Plane better.
Accommodation
Two-star hotel in centre of Madrid (old part). Price included breakfast. Other meals in cheap restaurants or bars. Excellent food. Hotel well located - everything within walking distance.
Visits and excursions
Most popular: Prado museum and trip to Toledo. Easter processions: interesting.
Bullfight: not very popular.

Revision 3

Grammar

1 Correct forms
1 we'd 2 sending 3 go
4 of going 5 despite 6 you
7 don't have to 8 would stop 9 can't
10 was sent

2 Verb tenses
1 won
2 found; was walking
3 is going to rain
4 arrived; had already started
5 have / 've just finished
6 would never have met
7 get / will get
8 would drive
9 was being served; had been waiting
10 listen

3 Key word transformations
1 could be working
2 wish Andrew was / were coming
3 are not allowed to ride
4 needn't / need not have booked
5 it is compulsory to stay
6 Nick was not / wasn't tall enough
7 will have to be cancelled
8 are being questioned by the
9 must have been Alison who
10 must / should be eaten

Vocabulary

1 Correct words
1 got on; rode 2 take 3 trip 4 mind
5 heavy 6 oven 7 lie 8 rises
9 stole 10 scar

2 Word building
1 a competitor 2 a psychologist
3 a resident 4 an actor / actress
5 an operator 6 a burglar
7 a civil servant 8 a chemist
9 a lawyer 10 an electrician

3 Phrasal verbs
1 d dropped (him) off
2 h lets (me) down
3 a put (you) up
4 j has been looking forward to
5 b is putting (me) off
6 e put (it) out
7 g 'll pick (you) up
8 i brought (the subject) up
9 f came across
10 c get on with

Unit 13

Reading

1 Before you read
You were probably able to answer questions 1, 2 and 3 but unable to answer 4. For your interest, 1 April 1933 was a Saturday.

2 Reading
1 Autism is a mental disease which prevents sufferers from communicating with the outside world.
2 1943
3 Between two and four out of every 10,000 people
4 _Rain Man_

3 Comprehension
1 C _... in other areas many of the children can use their brains in ways which are almost super-human._ (lines 11-13)
2 B
3 A _... about 85% of all recorded cases are male._ (lines 37-38)
4 B _The subject became the focus of particular media interest ..._ (line 49)
5 D

4 Vocabulary
A 1 illness (line 5)
2 exceptional; remarkable; amazing (lines 28; 29; 32)
3 skill; talent (lines 14; 28)
B 1 d 2 a 3 b 4 c 5 e
C calendrical, formal, exceptional, architectural, mathematical, medical, mechanical, controversial
D comical, intellectual, cultural, financial, educational, industrial

Grammar

1 Use of English
1 too 2 the 3 by 4 was 5 but
6 about 7 himself 8 an 9 to 10 and
11 could 12 their 13 of 14 can
15 not / hardly

2 Use of English
1 not as / so good at drawing
2 Jenny managed to catch
3 the fastest I am (I'm) able
4 (was) capable of winning
5 would probably be able to
6 knew how to cook
7 did not (didn't) succeed in convincing
8 would not (wouldn't) have been able

3 Find the mistakes
1 aren't I? 2 will you?
3 didn't we darling? 4 √
5 were they? 6 will you?
7 √ 8 do I?
9 √ 10 wouldn't you?

4 Use of English
1 have 2 time 3 to 4 that
5 of 6 √ 7 too 8 like
9 us 10 that 11 had 12 √
13 both 14 √ 15 the 16 √

Vocabulary

1 Use of English
1 popularity 2 extremely 3 harmless
4 damaging 5 dissatisfied 6 exceptions
7 traditionally 8 violence 9 growth
10 easily

2 Phrasal verbs
1 down 2 deposit 3 off 4 debt
5 instalments 6 out 7 loan 8 interest
9 up 10 salary 11 back 12 owed

3 Wordsearch

```
P R O S P E R O U S I
E Y A P W E T I P C C
N O M E A N O X S R A
S T I N G Y O E S E W
I P V D E B T V A D B
O W I T H D R A W I T
N E T T P U R S E T O
```

1 pension   2 withdraw 3 save   4 net
5 prosperous 6 debt   7 pay   8 wage
9 credit   10 rise   11 mean 12 tip
13 purse   14 stingy

4 Verbs of seeing

1 Scan   2 glance   3 staring
4 see   5 caught a glimpse 6 was looking
7 observed 8 notice

5 Opposites

1 generous   2 withdraw   3 borrow
4 worthless   5 wealthy

Writing

Applications

A Yes. The applicant is a foreign student and wants to do a Master's degree in English Literature at a British university.

B 1 B   2 D   3 B   4 C
    5 D   6 C   7 A   8 B

Unit 14

Reading

3 Comprehension

1 G   2 F   3 B   4 H
5 C   6 E   7 A
You do not need to use heading D.

4 Prepositions

1 aim **for**
2 work **through**
3 write **on** paper
4 **on** exam days
5 stick **to** a decision
6 **on** a daily basis
7 write **in** capital letters
8 stick something **on** a wall
9 **from** my angle
10 record **on** cassette

Grammar

1 Cause and effect

Possible answers:
2 Overwork results / can result in tiredness and stress.
3 Exercise makes you fit.
4 Eating too much sugar causes / can cause toothache.
5 Dangerous driving causes / can cause accidents.
6 Smoking causes / can cause heart disease.
7 African music makes you want to dance.
8 Holidays make you relax.
9 Listening to too much loud music can result in deafness.

2 Purpose

Possible answers:
2 Some people have winter holidays **so that they can** learn to ski.
3 People watch the news on TV **so as to** find out what's happening in the world.
4 Motorcyclists wear helmets **to** protect their heads.
5 Some young people start smoking **to** be like other people of their age.
6 Spiders make webs **in order to** catch their food.
7 Some people go to university **so that they will** improve their chances of getting a good job.

8 Some people have large dogs as pets **in order to** protect their homes against burglars.

3 Have / get something done

2 Yesterday I went to the optician's to **have my eyes tested.**
3 This afternoon I'm going to the dentist's **to have two teeth taken out.**
4 Last week I went to the doctor's to **have my blood pressure taken.**
5 Next Saturday I'm going to the vet's to **have my dog vaccinated.**
6 The day before yesterday, I went to the garage to **get my car serviced.**
7 Last year I went to the architect to **have a new house designed.**
8 Next week I'm going to the accountant to **have my annual accounts done.**

4 Use of English

1 out 2 of 3 but 4 a 5 √
6 been 7 √ 8 √ 9 have 10 which
11 to 12 √ 13 be 14 was 15 the

5 Use of English

1 that 2 or 3 if / whether 4 to
5 how 6 it 7 a 8 where
9 each 10 were 11 had 12 of
13 the 14 is 15 has

Vocabulary

1 People and places in education

```
              9
              L
1  P U P I L
2      H E A D
3      S E C O N D A R Y
4  I N F A N T
5      N U R S E R Y
6      B O A R D I N G
7      U N D E R G R A D U A T E
8  U N I V E R S I T Y
```

2 Health

1 SURGEON
2 OPERATING THEATRE
3 MIDWIFE
4 PATIENT
5 WARD
6 SURGERY

3 Use of English

1 commonly 2 infections 3 quickly
4 treatment 5 prescription 6 gently
7 unwell 8 immediately

4 Phrasal verbs

1 False: *put up with* = tolerate. It should say *put someone up (for the night).*
2 True
3 True
4 False: *get away with* = escape. It should say *get on with.*
5 False: *coming up against* = meeting something difficult. It should say *coming up with.*
6 True
7 False: *catch up with* = draw level with someone you are following. It should say *if you can't catch what someone says …*
8 True

Writing

Stories

A The words in bold are examples of descriptive language added to the original story.

A visit to the dentist

I woke up on Saturday night with toothache. **I felt terrible.** All day Sunday the pain got worse, so on Monday morning, **feeling desperate,** I telephoned the dentist and made an appointment.

I arrived at the surgery fifteen minutes early. There was nobody else in the **large, draughty** waiting room and there were no magazines to read. Time

passed **incredibly** slowly. **I felt a mixture of pain and fear.**

Eventually my name was called and I went in. Mr Parbury asked me to sit down. **He was a plump, middle-aged man with thick glasses and a kind voice.** He examined me **slowly and carefully** and said that one of my teeth would have to come out. He gave me an injection, took out the tooth and ten minutes later I left the surgery. **I was thankful that the pain had gone, and relieved that my visit was over.**

Revision 4

Grammar

1 Verb tenses

1 always had
2 will be / are travelling; arrives
3 waiting; wait; come
4 had been working / had worked
5 won't / will not be
6 will have been married
7 to send; were
8 are going to / will be lying
9 to stand
10 am going to faint

2 Key word transformations

1 didn't succeed in finishing
2 you know how to
3 so that I could hear
4 can make you / people ill
5 don't have to be
6 had his car fixed by / 's car was fixed by
7 didn't eat as much
8 never stayed at such a
9 is not / isn't as cheap as
10 am interested in applying

3 Correct forms

1 laugh   2 get my shoes repaired
3 so that he wouldn't 4 not to
5 will   6 enough food
7 Despite; managed 8 otherwise
9 was   10 have had

4 Expressing ability

1 have you been able to
2 can (is able to)
3 could (was able to)
4 to be able to / I'll be able to
5 couldn't (wasn't able to)
6 could
7 were able to
8 wouldn't have been able to
9 was able to
10 haven't been able to

Vocabulary

1 Correct words

1 take 2 gave 3 theatre 4 salaries
5 plays 6 to 7 scored 8 go
9 average 10 Package

2 Word building

A 1 unemployment 2 discourage
    3 hesitation 4 capability / capacity
    5 sympathy 6 separation
    7 investment 8 application; applicant
    9 mysterious 10 illness
B 1 illness 2 investment
    3 hesitation 4 mysterious
    5 unemployment 6 separation
    7 sympathy 8 capabilities / capacities
    9 applicants 10 discourage

3 Phrasal verbs

1 to pay off   2 bring (it) back
3 has gone off   4 is going on
5 pay (it) back   6 are brought on
7 to bring up   8 have put up
9 will go out   10 are bringing out